THE BEST BOOK OF Rugby Songs Ever!

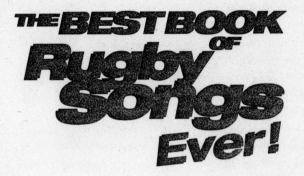

THE BEST BOOK OF Rugby Songs Ever!

CARLTON

CONTENTS

FOREWORD

YO! Large here...

And who better to make this song book a winner than me, being a Fatlad who likes his beer, loves his rugby and hates to lose. I love a good sing-song with the boys but only after I've sunk a jar or two and, surprisingly, then the words come a little easier.

So, the front row brigade don't need to pretend to know the words anymore 'coz they're here, all you have to do now is to perfect the "sneaky peak" as we've all done in church during the hymns. It's funny how you think people are always watching you sing and you're sure they would be more impressed if you looked like you knew the words. It's also funny how the girls in the backs always do...!?

I was taught my rugby at Blaydon RFC "Up North" and with that came my first lesson in boot polishing GONADS – I remember it took forever to get the stuff off. And with the boot polish came "Cushey Butterfield" and "the Hairs on her dickie diedo". Then I ventured to the big city, London, and Blackheath RFC where most of the songs were borrowed from Loughborough University and had to be sung one after the other with no rest and no chance of knowing the words.

But it wasn't until I went on the Easter tour to Cornwall with Biggus Dickus, the Old Dunstonaians and "When the coal comes home from Rhondda" that I realized that I had never really sung rugby songs before. These songs were very LARGE, but without really having to satisfy the Blacksmith's Wife. These songs were NOT RUDE!

So now I have songs for all occasions, that time straight after the game when children and ladies are around and later on when the Fatgirls come out to play. Sadly, Biggus Dickus is with us no longer, but I'm happy to say that Old Dunstonians are still touring Cornwall at Easter (65th this year), but he still lives on in the singing and the story telling.

Micky Skinner

TARZAN

Tarzan was a lazy old cock
Who went to sleep at seven o'clock
So tired was he, ooh, ahh, ahh
So tired was he, ooh, ahh, ahh
Along through the jungle he would go
Swinging his chopper to and fro
And along came a bee – a what? – a fucking great bee
Buzz, buzz, buzz, buzz, buzz, buzz, buzz
Fuck off bee, I ain't no rose and I ain't no syphilitic tree
Get off my nose, get off my organ
Don't you fucking come near me
If you want some fanny
You can fuck my granny
But there ain't no arseholes here, no fear.

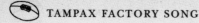
TAMPAX FACTORY SONG

Chrous:
Singing long ones, short ones, tampax factory,
Fat ones, thin ones, some the size of me

Verse 1:
You can tell by the smell
That she isn't very well
When the end of the month comes around

Repeat chorus

Verse 2:
You can tell by the chair
That she's been sitting there
When the end of the month comes around

Verse 3:
You can tell by the complexion
That your wasting your erection
When the end of the month comes around

Verse 4:
You can tell by the rope
That you haven't got a hope
When the end of the month comes around

Verse 5:
You can tell by the frown
That you'll have to go for brown
When the end of the month comes around

Verse 6:
You can tell by the moaning
That she's seeping haemoglobin
When the end of the month comes around

Verse 7:
You can tell by the taste
That it isn't salmon paste
When the end of the month comes around

Verse 8:
You can tell by the legs
That's she lost a few eggs
When the end of the month comes around

Verse 9:
You can tell it's a farce
When you shag her up the arse
When the end of the month comes around

Verse 10:
You can tell by her block
That you'll get a bloody cock
When the end of the month comes around

Verse 11:
You can tell by her dress
That her cunt is in a mess
When the end of the month comes around

Last verse:
So how can you blame us when we shag her up the anus
When the end of the month comes around?

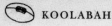

KOOLABAH

Early one morning, as the sun was rising, see a little engine
pull away
See a little driver, pull a little lever, chuff, chuff, chuff and away
we go
Down by the sea, where the water melons grow
I do my own, I dare not go
But if I do -oo, -oo
My mother will say, -ay, -ay
Have you ever seen a girl with green eyes down by the sea
See how she runs, see how she runs,
Koolabah, koolabah, sing, sing, sing

Who are, who are, who are we ?
We are (*insert club name*) RFC
We can struggle, we can fight
We can play the game all right
(*all shout club name*)

BIG RED ROSE

(to the tune of *When you were a tulip*)

She wore her panties, her pretty pink panties
And I wore my BVDs
First I caresses her, and then I undresses her
What a thrill she gave to me
I played with her boobies, her great big, white boobies
And down where the short hair grows
What could be sweeter as I played with my peter
And white-washed her big red rose?

RODRIGUEZ THE MEXICAN PERVERT

Chorus:
Eii-yii-yii-yii
Rodriguez the Mexican pervert
He'll eat out your mother and cornhole your brother
And waltz you around by the willy

Verse 1:
I was once the King of Spain
Who for women just didn't give a damn
But my pride and my joy
Was a round-bottomed boy
They say I'm a bugger and I am

Repeat chorus

Verse 2:
There once was a rugger named McNally
Who called on his team for a late rally
For each try that we score
I'll eat out a whore
And I'll start with my grandmother, Sally

Verse 3:
There once were three nuns from Birmingham
And this is the story concerning them
They lifted the frock
And they played with the cock
Of the Bishop as he was confirming them

Verse 4:
But the bishop was nobody's fool
He'd been to an English public school
He dropped his britches
And he fucked those bitches
With a 12-inch Episcopal tool

Verse 5:
There once was a man from Boston
Who drove a bright, red Austin
There was room for his ass
And a gallon of gas
But his balls hung out and he lost 'em

Verse 6:
There once was a girl named Alice
Who used a dynamite stick for a phallic
They found her vagina
In North Carolina
And parts of her tits in Dallas

Verse 7:
There once was a man from Dover in Kent
Whose monster dick was so long that it bent
He said with a grin
As he wiped cum off his chin
If my ear were a cunt then I'd fuck it

Verse 8:
I once knew a fellow named Urchin
Who was constantly jerkin' his gerkin'
His mother said Urchin
Quit jerkin' your gerkin'
Some day you'll need it for ferkin'

Verse 9:

There once was a man from Devises
Whose balls were of two different sizes
One was so small
It was nothing at all
But the other was big and won prizes

Verse 10:

There once was a man named Dave
Who kept a dead whore in a cave
She was shrivelled and shrunk
And God how she stank
But think of the money he saved

Verse 11:

There once was a man named Rock
Who played the string bass with his cock
He played such legato
And also spicatto
That he broke all the straps to his jock

Verse 12:

There once was a man from Sydney
Who could put it up to her kidneys
But a man from Quebec
Could put it up to her neck
Oh, but he had a big one, didn't he?

Verse 13:

There once was a man from Rangoon
Who was born nine months too soon
He didn't have the luck
To be born by a fuck
For he was scrapped off the sheets with a spoon

Verse 14:
There once was a man from Ealing
Who pounded his meat with great feeling
Then like a trout
He'd stick his mouth out
And wait for the drops from the ceiling

Verse 15:
There once was a man named Schwartz
Whose dick was all covered in warts
But the girls didn't care
About the warts that were there
'Cos Schwartz used to come in quarts

Verse 16:
There once was a lady from Cape Cod
Who thought all babies came from God
But it wasn't the almighty
Who laid it inside her
It was Roger the Dodger, by God

IF I WERE THE MARRYING KIND

If I were the marrying kind, I thank the Lord I'm not, sir
The kind of girl that I would wed would be a full-back's daughter
'Cos I'd find touch, she'd find touch
We'd both find touch together
We'd be all right in the middle of the night
Finding touch together

If I (*etc*)... would be a winger's daughter
'Cos I'd go hard, she'd go hard
We'd both go hard together
We'd be all right in the middle of the night
Going hard together

If I (*etc*) ... would a be centre's daughter
'Cos I'd pass out, she'd pass out
We'd both pass out together
We'd be all right in the middle of the night
Passing out together

If I (*etc*) ... would be a fly-half's daughter
'Cos I'd whip it out, she'd whip it out
We'd both whip it out together
We'd be all right in the middle of the night
Whipping it out together

If I (*etc*) ... would be a scrum-half's daughter
'Cos I'd put it in, she'd put it in
We'd both put it in together
We'd be all right in the middle of the night
Putting it in together

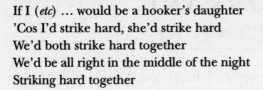

If I (*etc*) … would be a hooker's daughter
'Cos I'd strike hard, she'd strike hard
We'd both strike hard together
We'd be all right in the middle of the night
Striking hard together

If I (*etc*) … would be a tight head's daughter
'Cos I'd hold it up, she'd hold it up
We'd both hold it up together
We'd be all right in the middle of the night
Holding it up together

If I (*etc*) … would be a loose head's daughter
'Cos I'd bind tight, she'd bind tight
We'd both bind tight together
We'd be all right in the middle of the night
Binding tight together

Other verses:
Second row's daughter/'Cos I'd push hard…

Referee's daughter/'Cos I'd blow hard…

Groundsman's daughter/'Cos I'd trim bush…

Spectator's daughter/'Cos I'd not come…

Goalpost's daughter/'Cos I'd stand erect…

Rugby ball's daughter/'Cos I'd get handled…

Half-time orange's daughter/'Cos I'd get sucked…

I DON'T WANT TO JOIN THE ARMY

Chorus:
I don't want to join the army
I don't want to go to war
I'd rather hang around Piccadilly Underground
Living off the earnings of a high-class lady

I don't want a bayonet up my arsehole
I don't want my bollocks shot away
I'd rather stay in England,
In ruddy, bloody England
And fornicate my fuckin' life away, gor blimey

Verse:
Monday I touched her on the ankle
Tuesday I touched her on the knee
On Wednesday much success, I lifted up her dress
Thursday I saw it, gor blimey!
Friday I put my hand upon it
Saturday she gave my balls a tweak
And on Sunday after supper, I rammed the bugger up her,
And now she wants it seven days a week

Repeat chorus

Women's version:
I don't want to be a housewife,
I'd much rather be a whore
I'd rather turn some tricks, involving foot long pricks
Housework is a bore, gor blimey

I don't want to do his laundry
I don't want to cook his fucking food
And if I'm getting laid
I should be getting paid
Or else I must be truly getting screwed, gor blimey

THESE FOOLISH THINGS REMIND ME OF YOU, DEAR

Chorus:
These foolish things remind me of you, dear

Verse:
A daisy chain upon a Harley chopper
Your little sister with two giant whoppers
You had no tampax, just a rubber stopper

Repeat chorus:

Naked photographs of Liberace
The fragrant odour of your rotten crotchy
Syphilitic scabs that make your face so blotchy

A bloody tampax in the toilet bowl
The little round ring around your gaping hole
A pubic hair on my breakfast roll

The year we went to Edinburgh zoo
You fucked a rhino and a kangaroo
Tossed off a bear, your hair was filled with goo

Fresh defiled virgin on a marble slab
A toothless blowjob in a London cab
The pus that oozes from your vaginal scabs

Steaming semen on Lorna Doone
Your arsehole farted out a catchy tune
Cunnilingus, ate it with a spoon

Two tons of titty in a brass brassiere
Your twat that twitches like a moose's ear
A wad of semen floating in my beer

Head up my arsehole and you had to sneeze
Your mass of pubic hairs that harbour fleas
Your recipe for mellow foreskin cheese

Steaming mucus from your bulbus beezer
Masturbation with a pair of tweezers
Afterbirth fresh frozen from the freezer

The rugby party in the old hayloft
The team applauded as you sucked me off
The hard black steam, the blast that made you cough

Fucking rabbits in the forest grass
Psychotic blow jobs from a psychopath
A thousand crabs that drowned in your bath

A rusty dildo that gave you quite a shock
We stopped the bleeding with an old sweat sock
Aborted foetus pickled in a crock

The tasty orifices of your nose
The gooey breakfast from between your toes
The soiled crotch of your panty hose

Infected pimple that looks like rosey rubys
Symmetric stretch marks around your sagging boobies
You picked your nose and then you ate you goobies

Ovarian cysts for which they made incisions
Saturday nights of genital collisions
A vegematic for my circumcision

We like to butt fuck underneath my car
You get excited with a chocolate bar
Diarrhoea preserved in a pickle jar

ENGINEER SONG

(to the tune of *Old Hundred*)

An engineer told me before he died
Ah-hum, titty-bum, titty-bum, titty-bum
An engineer told me before he died
Ah-hum, Ah-hum
An engineer told me before he died
I have no reason to believe he lied
Ah-hum, titty-bum, titty-bum, titty-bum
Ah-hum, titty-bum, titty-bum, titty-bum

He had a wife with cunt so wide
Ah-hum, titty-bum, titty-bum, titty-bum
He had a wife with cunt so wide
Ah-hum … *etc*
He had a wife with cunt so wide
That she could never be satisfied
Ah-hum … *etc*

Other verses:
So he built a bloody great wheel
With two balls of brass and a prick of steel

The balls of brass he filled with cream
And the whole fucking issue was driven by steam

He tied her to the leg of the bed
Tied her hands above her head

There she lay demanding a fuck
He shook her hand and wished her luck

Round and round went the bloody great wheel
In and out went the prick of steel

Up and down went the level of steam
Down and down went the level of cream

Till at last the maiden cried
Enough, enough, I'm satisfied

Now we come to the tragic bit
There was no way of stopping it

She was split from arse to tit
And the whole fucking issue was covered in shit

It jumped off her, it jumped on him
And then it buggered their next of kin

It jumped on a town centre bus
And the mess it made caused quite a fuss

The last time, Sir, that prick was seen
It was over in England fucking the Queen

Nine months later a child was born
With two brass balls and a bloody great horn

The moral of this story is mighty clear
Never fuck an engineer

LIFE PRESENTS A DISMAL PICTURE

(to the tune of *Deutschland Uber Alles*)

Life presents a dismal picture
Dark and dreary as a tomb
Father's got an anal stricture
Mother's got a prolapsed womb

Uncle James has been deported
For a homosexual crime
Nell, our maid, has just aborted
For the forty-second time

Ours is not a happy household
No one laughs or even smiles
Mine's a dismal occupation
Crushing ice for Grandpa's piles

Jane the under-housemaid vomits
Every morning just at eight
To the horror of the butler
Who's the author of her fate

Auntie Kate has diarrhoea
Shits ten times more than she ought
Stands all day beside the rear
Lest she should be taken short

Grandpa, lurking in the woodshed,
Found a foetus in a case
Father Pike says it's murder
Of sister Annie there's no trace

Mabel's husband's now in prison
For a childish prank of mine
Pinching things that wasn't his
And women's panties off a line

Dad's a man who likes the bestial
Incest is my mother's fun
So the whole four of us sleep together
Father, mother, horse and son

Anal-oral trends disgust me
Though pronounced in Tiny Tim
For I much prefer fellatio
He sucks me and I suck him

Little Jim keeps masturbating
Though we tell him it's a sin
Uncle Dave's the Shrewsbury Slasher
Uncle Henry dobbed him in

Joe the postman called this morning
Stuck his penis through the door
We could not despite endearment
Get it out till half past four

Even now the baby's started
Having epileptic fits
Every time it coughs, it spews
Every time it farts, it shits

Yet we are not broken hearted
Neither are we up the spout
Cousin Sally has just farted
Turned her arsehole inside out

BITCH A DOG

(To the tune of *Do, Re, Mi*)

Bitch, a dog, a female dog
Itch, a place for you to scratch
Hitch, I pull my knickers up
Grab, another word for snatch
Bath, a place for making gin
Sex, another word for sin
Prick, a needle going in
And that will bring us back to
Bitch, bitch, bitch, bitch...

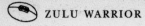

ZULU WARRIOR

Ole zooma zooma zooma
Ole zooma zooma chief
Drink it down you Zulu warrior
Drink it down you Zulu chief
Drink it down you Zulu warrior
Drink it down you Zulu chief, chief, chief

THE MAYOR OF BAYSWATER

(to the tune of *Deutschland Uber Alles*)

Opening verse:
The Mayor of Bayswater
He has a lovely daughter
And the hairs on her dickie-di-do
Hang down to her knees

Chorus:
And the hairs
And the hairs
And the hairs on her dickie-di-do
Hang down to her knees
One black one, one white one
And one with a little shite on
And the hairs of her dickie-di-do
Hang down to her knees

If she were my daughter
I'd have them cut shorter
And the hairs ... *etc*

Repeat chorus

I've smelt it, I've felt it,
It's just like a piece of velvet

Repeat chorus

I've seen it, I've seen it
I've laid right between it

I could not believe my eyes
When I pissed between her thighs

She came from Glamorgan
With a pussy like a barrel organ

She slept with a demon
Who washed her with semen

She lived on a mountain
And fucked like a bloody fountain

She stayed on a cattle ranch
And came like a bloody avalanche

She says she's no whore
But she bangs like a shit-house door

She married an Italian
With balls like a bloody stallion

It'd take a brontosaurus
To eat her clitoris

It'd take a Yorkshire miner
To find her vagina

It'd take a bloody wrecker
To extract your poor pecker

She lived on strawberry milkshake
And fucked like a bloody rattlesnake

She stayed in Seattle
And went down on cattle

I've stroked 'em, I've poked 'em
I've even rolled them up and smoked 'em

She sits on the beachfront
With the waves lapping at her cunt

I've licked it, I've kissed it
It tastes like a chocolate biscuit

You can drive a Mini Minor
Right up her vagina

Her vagina was squishy
And tasted a bit fishy

The aroma it lingers
It smells like fish fingers

I fucked her, I sucked her
I even loose rucked her

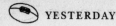

YESTERDAY

Yesterday
All my muscles seemed to feel OK
Now my body doesn't work today
Oh I went training yesterday

Muscles ache
They'd be better if I stayed in bed
Now it feels as if they're made of lead
Wish I'd stayed at home yesterday

Why did I run that mile
It felt so vile
But what the heck
Now it's clear
I'm a mere physical wreck

Bloodshot eyes
And my tongue is twice its normal size
It's at times like these I realize
Drinking isn't all that wise

Why I drank that beer
Isn't really clear
It's just a blur
I don't feel so young
And my tongue is lined with fur

Yesterday
Rugby seemed a healthy game to play
Now my body is in disarray
Oh I went rucking yesterday
mmmm-mmm-mmmmm

THE SEXUAL LIFE OF A CAMEL

Chorus:

Singing rump titty-titty, rump titty-titty, titty-rump
Singing rump titty-titty, rump titty-titty, hey
Singing rump titty-titty, rump titty-titty, titty-rump
The arsehole is here to stay

Verses:

Oh, the sexual life of a camel
Is stranger than anyone thinks
In the height of the mating season
He tries to bugger the Sphinx
But the Sphinx's posterior orifice
Is clogged by the sand of the Nile
Which accounts for the hump on the camel
And the Sphinx's inscrutable smile

Though the process of syphilization
From anthropoid ape down to man
It's been generally held that the Navy
Has buggered whatever it can
But in recent intensive researches
By Darwin and Huxley and Hall
It's been proved beyond doubt that the hedgehog
Has never been buggered at all

We therefore believe our conclusion
Is incontrovertibly shown
That relative safety on shipboard
Is enjoyed by the hedgehog alone
Why haven't they done it at Spithead

As they've done it at Harvard and Yale
And also at Oxford and Cambridge
By shaving the spines of its tail.

Alas my name is Cecil
I live in Leicester Square
I wear a flowered waistcoat
And a rosebud in my hair
For we're all queers together
Excuse us while we go upstairs (in pairs)
For we're all queers together
For arsehole is here to stay

While riding on the Underground
There wasn't a seat to be had
A young man offered me his seat
So I took it in my hand
For we're all queers together
Excuse us while we go up upstairs (in pairs)
For we're all queers together
The arsehole is here to stay

The sexual life of an Ostrich
Is stranger than that of a man
In the height of the mating season
He buries his head in the sand
When along comes a male of the species
And sees that big arse in the air
Does he care if it's male or female
Or doesn't he bloody well care

'Twas Christmas Eve in the Abbey
The Eunuchs all lined the stairs
Watching the fair young maidens

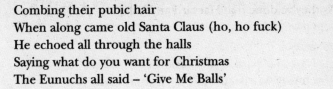

Combing their pubic hair
When along came old Santa Claus (ho, ho fuck)
He echoed all through the halls
Saying what do you want for Christmas
The Eunuchs all said – 'Give Me Balls'

– leads on to next song –

BALLS TO YOUR PARTNER

Chorus:
Balls to your partner, arse against the wall
If you've never been laid on Saturday night
You've never been laid at all.

Verses:
First lady forward, second lady back
Third lady's finger up the fourth lady's crack

Repeat chorus

The Queen was in the chamber, eating bread and honey
The King was in the chamber maid, and she was in the money

The Count and Countess they were there, a-doing it on the stair
The railings broke and down they fell, they finished in mid-air

The village butcher he was there, the cleaver in his hand
And every time he turned around he circumcized a man

The village harlot she was there, she was having fits
Swinging from the chandeliers and bouncing off her tits

The village postman he was there, but he had the pox
He couldn't do it with the ladies so he did the letter box

The village magician he was there, up to his usual tricks
He pulled his foreskin over his head and disappeared up his prick

The village cripple he was there, he wasn't up to much
He lined them up against the wall and fucked them with his crutch

The village economist he was there, pecker in his hand
Waiting for the moment when supply would meet demand

The village prostitute she was there, lying on the floor
Everytime she spread her legs the suction closed the door

The village bride she was there, explaining to the groom
The vagina not the rectum is the entrance to her womb

The village mystic he was there, climbing up the walls
He wanted a fuck, but was out of luck, for he had crystal balls

Little Joseph he was there, the leader of the choir
He kicked the boys in the balls to make their voices higher

The chimney sweep he was there, they had to throw him out
For every time he passed wind the room was filled with soot

The parson's daughter she was there, the cunning little runt
With poison ivy up her arse and thistle up her cunt

Tiny Thomas he was there, what do you think of that?
Amusing himself by abusing himself and catching it in a hat

Mr Jamieson he was there, the one that fought the Boers
He jumped upon the table and he shouted for the whores

John the blacksmith he was there, he wouldn't play the game
He did a lady seven times, and left her feeling lame

Little Eric he was there, he was having fun
Swinging from banisters and bouncing off his buns

The village carpenter he was there, looking like a fool
He brought his saw, he brought his hammer, but he forgot his tool

The village mortician he was there, quite out of breath
While fucking a stiff it farted, and it scared him half to death

Bobbing for apples his wife was there, fun to screw around
When the village idiot tried it, the stupid fucker drowned

Little Johnny he was there, he was only eight
He couldn't have the women so he had to masturbate

Willie Randle he was there, at the hot-dog stand
A grin upon his face and a sausage in his hand

Mrs Randle she was there, sitting on a bed
Weaving prophylactics from a spool of rubber thread

There was fucking on the couches, fucking on the cots
And lined up against the wall were rows of grinning twats

There was fucking in the fields, fucking in the oats
We were fucking women, but the Welsh were fucking goats

And when the ball was over everyone confessed
They all enjoyed the dancing, but the fucking was the best

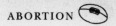

ABORTION

Verses:
Abortion, Abortion
A, B, O, R, T, I, O, N
Abortion, Abortion
A, B, O, R, T, I, O, N
Meat cleaver, coat hanger or a long pole
The thing that works the best is a can of draino

Scrotum, Scrotum
S, C, R, O, T, U, M
etc
It's baggy and it's scraggy and it's covered with hair
But what would you do if it wasn't there?

Nose job, Nose job
N, O, S, E, J, O, B
etc
It's better than a blowjob 'cos she doesn't cough
My baby loves it best when she sniffs me off

Tit fuck *etc*
Northside, southside, eastside or west
My baby loves it best when I come on her chest

Blow job *etc*
Northside, westside, eastside or south
My baby loves it best when I come in her mouth

Sick dick *etc*
All she wanted was a little kiss
But I ended up giving her syphilis

Jar fuck *etc*
It's warm and it's juicy and it'll even quiver
When you can't find a girl, use a jar of liver

Poop pack *etc*
It's round and it's brown and it's covered with goop
My baby loves it best when I pack her poop

Arse fuck *etc*
It's brown and it's round and it's full of gas
My baby loves it best when I fuck her up the arse

Eye fuck *etc*
Right eye, left eye, it's all the same
My baby loves it best when I come on her brain

Red lips *etc*
Life can be such a drag
When you're eating out your girl and she's on the rag

GOOD SHIP VENUS

(to the tune of *North Atlantic Squadron*)

Verse:
'Twas on the good ship Venus
By God you should have seen us
The figurehead was a whore in the bed
And the mast was a broken penis

Chorus:
Frigging on the rigging
Wanking on the planking
Masturbating on the grating
'Cos there's fuck all else to do

Other verses

The captain's wife was Mabel
Whenever she was able
She gave the crew their daily screw
Upon the galley table

Repeat chorus

The cabin's boy was Kipper
A cunning little nipper
He lined his arse with broken glass
And circumcized the skipper

The ladies of the nation
Arose in indignation
They stuffed his bum with chewing gum –
A smart retaliation

The ship's dog's name was Rover
The whole crew did him over
We ground and ground that faithful hound
From Singapore to Dover

The First Mate's name was Hopper
By God, he had a whopper
Twice round his neck, once round the deck
And up his arse for a stopper

The captain's randy daughter
She fell into the water
Delighted squeals revealed that eels
Had found her sexual quarter

'Twas on the China station
To roars of approbation
We sunk a junk with a load of spunk
By mutual masturabtion

The second mate's name was Carter
By God he was a farter
When the wind wouldn't blow and the ship wouldn't go
We'd get Carter the farter to start her

The cook whose name was Freeman
He was a dirty demon
He served the crew with menstrual stew
And foreskins fried in semen

The captain of that lugger
He was a dirty bugger
He wasn't fit to shovel shit

From one ship to another
On the trip to Buenos Aires
We rogered all the fairies
We got the syph at Tenerife
And a dose of clap in the Canaries

Another cook was O'Mally
He didn't dilly-dally
He shot his bolt with a hell of a jolt
And whitewashed half the galley

The captain was elated
The crew investigated
They found some sand in his prostrate gland
And he had to be castrated

The boatswain's name was Lester
He was a hymen tester
Through hymens thick he shoved his prick
And left it there to fester

The engineer was McTavish
And young girls he did ravish
His missing tool's at Istanbul
He was a trifle lavish

A gay boy was the purser
He couldn't have been worser
With all the crew he had a screw
Until they yelled 'No more, sir'

The ship's cat name was Hippy
His hole was black and shitty
But shit or not it had a twat

The captain showed no pity
So now we end this serial
Through lack of sheer material
We wish you luck and freedom from
Diseases venereal

CHAPPED HIDE

(to the tune of *Raw Hide*)

Ballin', ballin', ballin'
That boy he keeps on callin'
His crabs, they keep crawlin'
Chapped hide?

You thought he was the right one
But he was a one-night stand one
He'd shoot his blanks with his gun
Chapped hide!

Pick him up, take him home
Ride him hard, make him moan
Wake him up, saddle up, send him home
Chapped hide – Yee Haw!

ARSE HOLES FOR SALE

(to the tune of *La Donna in Mobile*)

Arse holes are cheap today
Cheaper than yesterday
Little ones are half a crown
Standing up or bending down

Larger ones are three and six
Because they have larger pricks
Arse holes are cheap today
Cheaper than yesterday

MY KIND OF GIRL

(to the tune of *British Grenadier*)

I like the girls who say they will
I like the girls who say they won't
I hate the girls who say they will
And then they say they won't
But of all the girls I like the best
I may be wrong or right
Are the girls who say they never will
But look as though they might

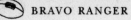

BRAVO RANGER

(to the tune of *Sound Off*)

I want to be a Bravo ranger
Live a life of fun and danger
Scuba diver
Sixty niner
I've got a girl and she's the best
Many a time I've sucked her breast
Fucked her standing
Fucked her lying
If she had wings
I'd fuck her flying
Now she's dead, but not forgotten
Dug her up and fucked her rotten

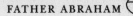

FATHER ABRAHAM

Chorus:
Father Abraham fucked seven squirrels
And seven squirrels fucked Father Abraham
And he never laughed
And he never cried
All he did was go like this

(with motions)
With a left (arm), with a left
With a right (arm), with a right
With a left (leg), with a left
With a right (leg), with a right
With a HOO (head), with a HOO
with an AHH (pelvis), with an AHH

Father Abraham (HUAH) fucked seven squirrels
And seven squirrels fucked Father Abraham (HUAH)
And he never laughed
And he never cried
All he did was go like this (HUAH)

BESTIALITY'S BEST

(to the tune of *Tie Your Kangaroo Down...*)

Bestiality's best, boys
Bestiality's best – fuck a wallaby
Bestiality's best, boys
Bestiality's best

Oh, put your log up a dog, Claude
Put your log up a dog – bestiality
Don't you fancy a dog, Claude
Put your log up a dog

Other verses

Stick your lug in a slug, Doug
Aren't you hot for a slug, Doug

Slip your slew in a ewe, Lou
Don't you dream of a ewe, Lou

Get turned on by a duck, Chuck
Don't it make you go quack, Chuck

Tickle the clit of a gnat, Matt
Isn't that just where it's at, Matt

Rough love with a horse, Boris
You gotta use force with a horse, Boris

Continue in the same vain, e.g.

Anyway you can with toucan, Bob...

Be a queer with a deer...

Be a rotter with an otter...

Be very pleasant to a pheasant...

Bring a flea to its knees...

Chuck your sperm in a worm...

Come from behind with a hind...

Cunnilingo with a dingo...

Do an illegal with an eagle...

Down the throat of a goat...

Drink the pee of a bee...

Lick the juice of a moose...

Drip your yeast on a wildebeest...

Ejaculate in a snake...

Get a suck from a duck...

Slap it out for a trout...

Get the pox off a fox...

Penetrate deep with a sheep...

Get your oats with some stoats...

Get your release in a fleece...

Give a licking to a chicken...

Give some cock to a croc...

Give your gerbil some verbal...

Grind your mound on a hound...

Have a lark with an aardvark...

Have a shaggin' with a dragon...

BIG BAMBOO

I asked my lady what I should do
To make her happy, not make her blue
She said, 'The only thing I want from you
Is a little bitty of the big bamboo'

She wanted the big bamboo, bamboo
Eye eye-eye eye-eye-eye
Working for the Yankee dollar

So I gave her a coconut
She said, 'I like him, he's OK
But there's just one thing that worries me
What good are the nuts without the tree?'

So I sold my lady a banana plant
She said, 'I like him, he's elegant
We should not let him go to waste
But he's much too soft to suit my taste'

So I bought my lady a sugar cane
The fruit of fruits, I did explain
But she was tired of him very quick
She said, 'I'd rather get my lips around your dip stick'

So I gave my honey a rambutan
Soft and prickly, how the juices ran
She said, 'I've seen a fruit like this before
But it had a long stalk and two pips in the core'

She met a chinaman, Him Hung Low
They got married, went to Mexico
But she divorced him very quick
She said 'I want bamboo, not chopstick'

BASTARD KING OF ENGLAND

(to the tune of *The Irish Washerwoman*)

Oh, the minstrels sing of an English king
Of many long years ago
He ruled his land with an iron hand
Though his mind was weak and slow
He loved to hunt the royal stag
Around the royal wood
But better by far he loved to sit
And pound the royal pud

Chorus:
He was lousy and dirty and covered in fleas
The hair on his balls hung down to his knees
And he had his women in two and threes
God bless the bastard King of England

Now the Queen of Spain was an amorous Jane
And a sprightly wench was she
She longed to fool with the royal tool
From far across the seas
So she sent a royal messenger
To invite the King of England down
To spend the night with her

Now ol' Philip of France he heard by chance
Within his royal court
And he swore 'She loves my rival best
Because my tool is short'
To give the Queen a dose of the clap
To pass it on, to the Bastard King of England

When the news of this foul deed was heard
Within the royal halls
The King he swore by the royal whore
He'd have the Frenchman's balls
He offered the royal purse
And a piece of the Queen's hortense
To any British subject who could do the King of France

So the noble Duke of Middlesex
He took himself to France
He swore he was a fairy
So the King let drop his pants
Then on Philip's dong he slipped a thong
Leapt on his horse and galloped along
Dragging the Frenchman back
To merry old England

When he returned to London Town
Within fair England's shores
Because of the ride King Philip's pride
Was stretched a yard or more
And all the silken drawers
Came down to London town
And shouted round the battlements
'To hell with the British crown'
And Philip alone usurped the throne
His sceptre was his royal bone
With which he ditched the bastard King of England

BARNACLE BILL

(to the tune of *Barnacle Bill the Sailor*)

Fair young maiden:
'Who's that knocking at my door?'
'Who's that knocking at my door?'
'Who's that knocking at my door?'
Said the fair young maiden

Barnacle Bill:
'It's Barnacle Bill from over the hill'
Said Barnacle Bill the sailor
'It's Barnacle Bill from over the hill'
Said Barnacle Bill the sailor

FYM: 'Why are you knocking at my door?' *etc*
BB: 'Cos I'm young enough and ready and tough *etc*

FYM: Shall I come and let you in? *etc*
BB: Open the door, you dirty old whore *etc*

FYM: Will you sleep upon the floor? *etc*
BB: Get off the floor, you dirty old whore *etc*

FYM: Will you sleep upon the mat?
BB: Bugger the mat, you can't fuck that *etc*

FYM: Will you sleep upon the stairs?
BB: Bugger the stairs they've got no hairs *etc*

FYM: Will you sleep upon my breasts? *etc*
BB: Bugger your tits they give me the shits *etc*

FYM: Will you sleep between my thighs? *etc*
BB: Cut the talk and open your fork *etc*

FYM: Will you sleep within my cunt? *etc*
BB: Bugger the cunt, but I'll fuck for a stunt *etc*

FYM: What if we should have a child? *etc*
BB: Smother the bugger and fuck for another *etc*

FYM: What if we should have a girl? *etc*
BB: We'll dig a ditch and bury the bitch *etc*

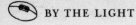

BY THE LIGHT

(to the tune of *By the Light of the Silvery Moon*)

By the light (by the light, by the light)
Of a flickering match
I saw her snatch
In the watermelon patch

By the light (by the light, by the light)
Of a flickering match
I saw it gleam, I heard her scream
You are burning my snatch
With your fucking match

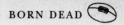

BORN DEAD

(to the tune of *Born Free*)

Born dead!
Your baby was born dead
All torso and no head
Born dead to live in a jar

Stay dead?
Don't come back to haunt me
You don't really want me
Born dead to live in a jar

Brain dead!
Your husband is brain dead
A vein popped in his head
That sucker's a mort

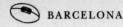

BARCELONA

(to the tune of *Mañana*)

Chorus:
Mañana, mañana
Is my banana good enough for you?

Way down in Barcelona
Where ladies learn to knit
A lady stuck a knitting needle in another lady's tit
Said the lady to the lady
'We're here to learn to knit
Not to stick a knitting needle in another lady's tit'

Way down in Barcelona
Where drummers play the drum
A drummer struck a drumstick up another drummer's bum
Said the drummer to the drummer
'We're here to play the drum
Not stick a drumstick up another drummer's bum'

Way down in Barcelona
Where lepers decompose
A leper picked a snotty from another leper's nose
Said the leper to the leper
'We're here to decompose
Not to pick a snotty from another leper's nose'

Way down in Barcelona
Where ladies learn to swim
A lady put her finger up another lady's quim
Said the lady to the lady
'We're here to learn to swim
Not to put our fingers up another lady's quim'

Way down in Barcelona
Where beggars beg for food
A beggar chucked a turd in another beggar's gruel
Said the beggar to the beggar
'We're here to beg for food
Not to chuck turds in another beggar's food'

Way down in Barcelona
Where the miners shovel coal
A miner shoved a shovel up another miner's hole
Said the miner to the miner
'We're here to shovel coal
Not to shove a shovel up another miner's hole'

Way down in good old London town
Where the cabbies drive so fast
A cabby rammed his cab up another cabby's arse
Said the cabby to the cabby
(*wind down window*)
FUCK OFF, WANKER!

WALRUS AND THE CARPENTER

If all the whores with crimson drawers
Came walking down the Strand
'Do you suppose,' the Walrus said
That we could raise a stand?'
'I doubt it,' said the carpenter
'But wouldn't it be grand' –
And all the while the dirty sod
Was coming in his hand

When you were only sweet sixteen
And you had a little quim
You stood before the looking glass
And put one finger in
But now that you are old and grey
And losing all your charm
I can get five fingers in
And half my fucking arm

AS I WAS WALKING

(to the tune of *Old One Hundredth*)

As I was walking through the wood
I shat myself, I knew I would
I cried for HELP but no help came
And so I shat myself again

As I was walking through St Paul's
The vicar grabbed me by the balls
I cried for HELP but no help came
And so he grabbed me by the balls again

As I was walking through St Giles
Some bastard grabbed me by the piles
I cried for HELP but no help came
And so he grabbed me by the piles again

As I was walking down the street
A whore grabbed me by the meat
I cried for HELP but no help came
And so she grabbed me by the meat again

As I lay sleeping in the grass
Some bastard rammed it up my arse
I cried for HELP but no help came
And so he rammed it up my arse again

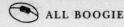

ALL BOOGIE

(to the tune of *Sound off*)

Chorus:
I boogied last night
And the night before
I'm going back tonight
And boogie some more

Verses:
Daddy's on the bottom
Mummy's on top
Baby's in the attic
Filling rubbers with snot

Mummy's on the bottom
Daddy's on top
Baby's in the cradle yelling
'Shove it to 'er pop'

Mummy's in the hospital
Daddy's in jail
Sister's in the corner
With her pussy for sale

I got a girl
'Bout six foot four
She fucks everything
Like a two-bit whore

I got a girl
She lives on a hill
She won't fuck
But her sister will

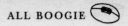

Daddy's got a watch
Mummy's got a ring
Sister's got a baby
From shaking that thing

One and one makes two
Two and two makes four
If the bed breaks down
We'll fuck on the floor

A FEW OF MY FAVOURITE THINGS

For the men:
Middle and pinky and index and ring
Throw in the thumb and you've got the whole thing
It works just fine and it's also quite safe
These are a few of my favourite things

When the dawn breaks
When I wake up
And it's feeling hard
I simply remember my favourite things
And that's when it feels so good

Penthouse and *Playboy* and something called *Forum*
They're what I use to help start it growing
Centrefolds spread eagled showing me pink
These are a few of my favourite things

When I'm lonely
Really lonely
By myself again
I simply remember my favourite things
And that's when it feels so good

For the women:
Dildos and vibrators and vaseline jelly
That's what I use to set fires in my belly
In and out, up and down, making me wet
These are a few of my favourite things

Men are useless
I don't need them
I'm the best I've had
I simply remember my favourite things
And that's when it feels so good

Tight buns, silk undies and erotic books
Make me excited and I'm starting to cook
I stir me up and the honey will come
These are a few of my favourite things

When I'm thinking
Of a hard cock
But I don't see one
I simply remember my favourite things
And that's when it feels so good

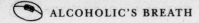

ALCOHOLIC'S ANTHEM

(to the tune of *Men of Harlech*)

What's the use of drinking tea
Indulging in sobriety
And teetotal perversity
It's healthier to booze
What's the use of milk and water
These are drinks that never oughta
Be allowed in any quarter
Come on, lose your blues
Mix yourself a shandy
Drown yourself in brandy
Sherry sweet
Or whiskey neat
Or any kind of piss that's handy
There's no fucking sense in drinking
Anything that doesn't make you stinking
There's no happiness like sinking
Wasted to the floor
Put an end to all frustration
Drinking may be your salvation
End it all in dissipation
Rotten to the core
Aberrations metabolic
Ceilings that are hyperbolic
These are for the alcoholic
Lying on the floor
Vodka for the arty
Lemonade was only made
For drinking if your mother's at the party
Steer clear of home-made beer
And anything that isn't labelled clear
There is nothing else to fear
Bottom's up, my boys

'A' YOU'VE GOT ARSEHOLE STAINS

A – you've got arsehole stains
B – you've got balls for brains
C – you've hardly got a cock at all
D – like a dorker's tool
E – your arse exudes stool
F – your farts smell like fucking shit
G – you've got ghonerrhea
H – haemorrhoids to your knees
I – eyes that run and bleed and itch
J – you can jerk your cock
K – you kiss my snatch
L – fucking lousy son-of-a-bitch
M-N-O-P – menstrual blood on your prick
Q-R-S-T – alphabetically speaking you're S-H-I-T
U – make my pussy itch
V – D down to your feet
W-X-Y-Z – I love to wander through the alphabet with you
to tell the world what you mean to me

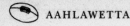

AAHLAWETTA

Chorus:
Aahlawetta, gentile aahlawetta
Aahlawetta je te plumerai

Leader:
Does she have ze stringy hair?

All:
Oui, she has ze stringy hair

Leader:
Stringy hair

All:
Stringy hair

Leader:
Aahlawett!, aah, aah, aah

Chorus

Leader:
Does she have ze furrowed brow?

All:
Yes she has ze furrowed brow

Leader:
Furrowed brow

All:
Furrowed brow

Leader:
Stringy hair

All:
Stringy hair

Leader:
Aahlawett! aah, aah, aah

Chorus

Other verses:
Broken nose
Blow job lips
Cum-stained teeth
Double chin
Swinging tits
Beer belly
Massive arse
Thunder thighs

Leader:
Now isn't she a very nice girl?

All:
Yes she is a very nice girl

Leader:
With the – (*Repeat all of the above*)

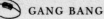

GANG BANG

(to the tune of *Billboard March*)

Chorus:
I love a gang bang, oh yes I do
'Cos a gang bang makes me feel so good
When I was younger and in my prime
I use to gang bang all the ti-i-ime
But now that I'm older and turning grey
I only gang bang twice a day

'Knock knock'

Response: Who's there?
Ida
Response: Ida who?
Ida want another gang bang

Other verses:
Ranger
Response: Ranger who?
Arranger for best entry at the gang bang

Oliver
Response: Oliver who?
All of her clothes were off at the gang bang

Peter Meter
Response: Peter Meter who?
My peter'll meet her for a gang bang

Ben
Response: Ben who?
Ben-d over and have another gang bang

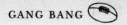

Dolly Parton
Response: Dolly Parton who
Dolly partin' her thighs at the gang bang

Bob
Response: Bob who
Bob down and let's have another gang bang

Yurin
Response: Yurin who?
Yurin for sloppy seconds at the gang bang

Kissinger
Response: Kissinger who?
Kissinger great, but fuckin' her is better at the gang bang

Betty
Response: Betty who?
Bet he'll have sore dick after the gang bang

Alexander
Response: Alexander who?
I licks under her ass at the gang bang

More verses:
Irish/I wish we were at the…
Virginia/Virgins are welcome at the…
Anita/I need a little rest at…
Sharon/Share and share alike at the…
Gladiator/Glad he ate her out before the…
Adolph/I ate off the bed at the…
Satellite/Sat a lot on her face at the…
Kenya/Can ya give me directions to the…
Mikey/I lost my keys to the handcuffs at the…

RUGBY, RACING AND BEER

When I was just a little kid
Knee high to a keg
My daddy put me on his knee
He drained his glass and closed his eyes
And gave me very sound advice
On how to be a good Kiwi

Get to know your rugby sides
And learn to spell from race guides
And don't forget down under over here
Because of your great tutelage
You have a great heritage
Of rugby, racing and beer

Chorus:
Rugby, racing and beer
Rugby, racing and beer
Down under they're mad over their
Rugby, racing and beer

Old Uncle Charlie went to see
The doctor yesterday
He cried, 'You've got to help me Doc and quick
I'm seeing spots before my eyes
My head feels twice its normal size
And every morning I feel sick'

The doctor took one look at him
and said, 'Well, Charlie, things look grim
I hate to have to tell you, but I fear
You'd better write your will tonight
'Cos you've got Kiwi-itis –
That's rugby, racing and beer'

WALKING DOWN CANAL STREET

Walking down Canal Street
Knocking on every door
Goddam son of a bitch
Couldn't find a whore

When I finally found a whore
She was tall and thin
Goddam son of a bitch
Couldn't get it in

When I finally got it in
I turned it all about
Goddam son of a bitch
Couldn't get it out

When I finally got it out
It was red and sore
Goddam son of a bitch
You should never fuck a whore

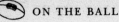

ON THE BALL

Chorus:
On the ball, on the ball, on the ball
Through scrummage, three quarters and all
By sticking together we keep on the leather
And shout as we go on the ball

Verse:
Well, some talk of soccer
And some talk of league
Some play cricket with a red shiny ball
But fighting together, we keep on the leather
And shout as we go on the ball

Repeat chorus

Remember my lads, as we journey through life
There's a goal to be reached by us all
By fighting together, we keep on the leather
And shout as we go on the ball

RUCK, RUCK WHEREVER YOU MAY BE

(to the tune of *Lord of the Dance*)

Chorus:
Ruck, ruck, wherever you may be
We are the boys of (*insert club name*) rugby
And we'll lead you down into debauchery
'Cos we are the boys of (*insert club name*) rugby

Verse:
We scrummed in the summer when the grass was green
The meanest fuckin' pack you ever have seen
We scrummed in the winter when the grass was gone
We are (*insert club name*) and the scrum goes on

Repeat chorus

Behind our forwards everything is well
Because our backs are the hounds of hell
They tackle hard, they run so fast
And in the sack they last and last

We have a coach, he brings us beer
If it wasn't for him, we wouldn't be here
Thanks to (*insert coach's name*) tender, loving care
The brew that sustains us is always there

Here's to the women that we hold dear
Why they stay with us it really isn't clear
We love and cherish them every one
But they'll always come second to a (*insert club name*) scrum

MY OLD MAN'S AN ALL BLACK

Chorus:
Oh, my old man's an All Black
He wears the silver fern
His mates just couldn't take him
So he's out now for a turn

Verse:
Well, Dad's played rugby all his life
And it's very plain to see
He's trying hard to make
An All Black out of me
'Son, don't you worry if you get
Punched when down in a scrum
Just wait, till there's a ruck
And you can fix the guilty one'

Repeat chorus

WHY WAS HE BORN SO BEAUTIFUL

Why was he born so beautiful
Why was he born at all
He's no fucking use to anyone
He's no fucking use at all

He ought to be publicly pissed on
He ought to be publicly shot (bang, bang)
He ought to be tied to a urinal
And left there to fester and rot

So, drink chug-a-lug
Drink chug-a-lug
Drink chug-a-lug
Drink

MARY ANN BARNES

Mary Ann Barnes is the Queen of the acrobats
She can do tricks that will give a man the shits
She can shoot green peas from her fundamental orifice
Do a double somersault and catch 'em on her tits
She's a great big fat shit, twice the size of me
Hair on her arse like the branches in a tree
She can swim, fight, shoot, fuck
Climb a tree or form a ruck
She's the kind of girl that's gonna marry me

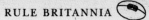

RULE BRITANNIA

Rule Britannia, marmalade and jam
Five Chinese crackers up your arsehole
BANG, BANG, BANG, BANG, BANG

Rule Britannia, Britannia rules the seas
Britons never, never, never will shit peas

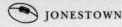

JONESTOWN

(to the tune of *Downtown*)

When you're down and you're broke, and your religion's a joke
Why don't you go and see
Jim Jones
When your life's incomplete, there's only one man to meet
Why don't you go and see
Jim Jones

Watch him mix the cool aid in the vat so lethal
Listen to the anguished cries of all the dying people
Everyone dies

The rev's the most gracious host
So, lift up your glasses, the ultimate toast
(So, lift up your glasses, the dirge of the masses)
Your in Jonestown
Chances are mighty slim
Jonestown
People are dropping like flies

Congressman Ryan, on a mission of spyin'
Would not drink with
Jim Jones
Such a public disgrace, they had to blow off his face
'Cos he would not drink with
Jim Jones

First you cough and then you wheeze, then you drop to your knees
From drinking cool aid with
Jim Jones
You arrive back in the States, decomposed in your crates
From drinking cool aid with
Jim Jones

I MET A WHORE IN THE PARK

(to the tune of *When Johnny Comes Marching Home*)

I met a whore in the park one day
Ya ho, ya ho
I met a whore in the park one day
Ya ho, ya ho
I met a whore in the park one day
She said, 'Hey boy you wanna lay'

Chorus:
Get in, Get out, quit fucking about
Ya ho, ya ho, ya ho

I put my hand upon her toe
Ya ho, ya ho
I put my hand upon her toe
Ya ho, ya ho
I put my hand upon her toe
She said, 'Hey boy you're way too low'

Repeat chorus

I put my hand upon her knee/She said hey boy you're kidding me
I put my hand upon her thigh/She said hey boy you're way too shy
I put my hand upon her tit/She said hey boy you're getting it
I put my hand upon her twat/She said hey boy you've hit the spot
I put my dick into her mouth/She said mm, mhmh, mhmhmh
I put her in a wooden box/From having to many young boy's cocks
I dig her up every now and then/She did me before she'll do
me again

YOGI BEAR

(to the tune of *Kempton Races*)

I know a bear that you all know
Yogi, Yogi
I know a bear that you all know
Yogi, Yogi bear
Yogi, Yogi bear
Yogi, Yogi bear
I know a bear that you all know
Yogi, Yogi bear

Yogi's got a little friend
Booboo, Booboo
Yogi's got a little friend
Booboo, Booboo bear
Booboo, Booboo bear
Booboo, Booboo bear
Yogi's got a little friend
Booboo, Booboo bear

Yogi's got a girlfriend, Suzi
Suzi, Suzi bear

Yogi's got an enemy, Ranger
Ranger, Ranger Smith

Yogi's got a cheesy knob, camem
Camem, Camembert

Suzi likes it on the fridge, polar
Polar, polar bear

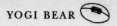

Booboo likes it up the arse, brown
Brown, brown bear
Suzi hates it up the arse, something
Something she can't bear

Yogi's dick is long and green, cucum
Cucum, cucumber

Suzi likes to shave her pubes, grizzly
Grizzly, grizzly bear

Yogi's got a two-foot knob, difficult
Difficult to bear

Booboo does it in a tree, koala
Koala, Koala bear

I DON'T WANT TO BE A SOLDIER

Oh, I don't want to be a soldier
I don't want to join the fightin' class
I just want to go
Down to old Soho
Pinchin' all the girlies in the shoulder blades
Oh, I don't want to see the Queen's Dominions
Why, London's full of girls I've never had
I just want to stay in England,
Jolly, jolly England
And follow in the footsteps of me dad

So call out the members of the Queen's Marines
Call out the King's Artillery
Call out me mother
Me sister and me brother
But for Christ sake's don't call me

I USED TO WORK IN CHICAGO

I used to work in Chicago in an old department store
I used to work in Chicago I don't work there anymore

A lady came in for a carpet
Some carpet from the store
Carpet she wanted, laid she got
I don't work there anymore

I used to work in Chicago in an old department store
I used to work in Chicago I don't work there anymore

A lady came in for some jewellery
Some jewellery from the store
Jewellery she wanted, a pearl necklace she got
And I don't work there anymore

Others include:
Paper she wanted ... A ream she got
Nail she wanted ... Screwed she got
Fishing rod she wanted ... My pole she got
Meat she wanted ... Sausage she got
Helicopter she wanted ... My chopper she got
Camel she wanted ... Hump she got
Translator she wanted ... Cunning linguist she got
Kitkat she wanted ... Four finger she got
Lamb she wanted ... Porked she got
Coke she wanted ... 7-UP she got
Turkey she wanted ... Stuffing she got
Ruler she wanted ... 12 inches she got
Policeman she wanted ... Truncheon she got
Milk she wanted ... Cream she got
Fuck she wanted ... Fuck she got

THERE WAS AN OLD LADY

Chorus:
Too-ra-li, too-ra-li, too-ra-lay, too-ra-lay
A rolling stone gathers no moss as they say
Sing along, sing along, with the birds, with the birds
It's a wonderful song, but it's all about turds

Verse:
There was an old lady who lived in the street,
Her passage was blocked up from too much to eat
She took stomach pills without reading the box
Before she could think turds were flying for blocks

Repeat chorus

Well she ran to the window and stuck out her arse
Just at that moment a policeman walked past
That poor old policeman was eating his pie
When a steaming hot turd hit him right in the eye

Well he ran to the east and he ran to the west
When a further consignment hit him right in the chest
Well he fled to the north and he fled to the south
When a bloody great turd hit him right in the mouth

The next time you walk over Waterloo bridge
Look out for a policeman asleep on the ridge
His chest bears a placard, around it these words
'Be kind to this copper who's been blinded by turds'

RING THE BELL VERGER

Chorus:
Ring the bell, Verger, ring the bell, ring
Perhaps the congregation will condescend to sing
Perhaps the village organist sitting on his stool
Will play upon his organ and not upon his tool

Verses:
Ocean liner five months late
Stoker stoking stoker's mate
Captain's voice comes down the wire
'Stop stoking mate and start stoking fire!'

Lordship's chauffeur in the garage lies
Lordship's wife between his thighs
Lordship's voice comes from afar
'Stop fucking wife and start the fucking car!'

Part-time barman in the White Horse lurks
Tossing off with erratic jerks
The landlord's voice begins to moan
'Stop pulling plonker and start pulling foam!'

Verger in the belfry stood
Grasped in his hand, his mighty pud
From afar the vicar yells
'Stop pulling pud and start pulling bells!'

Old time convict in the compound stands
His prick lies idle in his hands
The warden's voice begins to moan
'Stop pricking prick and start picking stone!'

SUPERCALLOUSFLAGELLISTI-CEXPECTCUNNILINGUS

Chorus:
Supercallousflagellisticexpectcunnilingus,
Queers like to take it up the bum from dildos, to dicks of fingers
Lesbians like their tonguing slow to make the climax linger
But Supercallousflagellisticexpectcunnilingus
Um-diddle-diddle-diddle, um-diddleye

My fat Auntie Ethel was into suits of rubber
Then she met the Michelin Man and took him as a lover
But they used a diesel tube for enemas on each other
The explosion rocked the city hall and covered it in blubber
Um-diddle-diddle-diddle, um-diddleye

Uncle John likes whips and knives and ladies to disfigure
Auntie Kath likes to be tied and whipped with bamboo canes or wicker
She said 'Whip me, whip me and make me writhe and slither'
He said 'No, I'll tickle you, that will make my dick get stiffer'
Um-diddle-diddle-diddle, um-diddleye

Uncle Cyril, we always knew, was into brown hattery
He stuck a dildo up his boyfriend's bum with lots of beer and flattery
'Take it out and I'll give you dick,' he said quite matter of factly
'Oh no, please don't take it out, but kindly change the battery'
Um-diddle-diddle-diddle, um-diddleye

Mary Jane looks like a man but on little girls she's keener
Thought she'd take a virgin home and try to go between her
The virgin said 'Oh no, please, sir
I don't know where it's been'
Mary Jane said, 'It's factory fresh' and introduced a wiener
Um-diddle-diddle-diddle, um-diddleye

MY MOTHER-IN-LAW

One night in Gay Paree
I paid five francs to see
A big fat French lady
Tattooed from head to knee
And on her jaw was a British man-o-war
And on her back was a Union Jack
So I paid her five francs more

And running up and down her spine
Was the BHB in line
And on her lily-white bum
Was a picture of the rising sun
And on her fanny
Was Al Johnson singing 'Mammy'
How I loves her, how I loves her
How I loves my mother-in-law

I loves my mother-in-law
She's nothing but a dirty old whore
She nags me day and night
And I can't do shit all right
She's coming home today
But I hope she stays away
Now isn't it a pity
She's only got one titty
And she's in the family way

Last night I greased the stairs
Put tin-tacks on the chairs
I hope she breaks her back
Because I do love wearing black

She drinks all my brandy
And makes my dog feel randy
How I loves her, how I loves her
How I loves my mother-in-law

MASTURBATION

(to the tune of *Alouette*)

Chorus:
Masturbation, I love masturbation
Masturbation, I love masturbation

Leader:
How I like to choke my chicken

All:
Yes, he likes to choke his chicken

Leader:
Choke my chicken

All:
Choke his chicken

Leader:
Masturbate

All:
Masturbate

Repeat chorus

(*There is now a new leader for each verse and all old verses should be repeated*)

Leader:
How I like to spank my monkey

All:
How he likes to spank his monkey

Leader:
Spank my monkey

All:
Spank his monkey

Leader:
Choke my chicken

All:
Choke his chicken

Leader:
Masturbate

All:
Masturbate

Other verses include:
Lope my mule
Rub my nub
Whip the lizard
Tease the beaver
Flog my log
Stroke my snake
Beat my meat
Pull my pony
Yank my chain
Shuffle the pack
Moan and jerk
Roger my todger

I'LL TAKE THE LEFT LEG

(to the tune of *Loch Lomond*)

Oh, I'll take the left leg and you take the right leg
It's my turn to give her the caber
'Cos me and my true love have never been the same
Since I shared her with the next door neighbour

When the Lord and his band were shaping up this land
They found that they had left over
A pile of useless crap on the left side of the map
That they'd hacked out of the white cliffs of Dover

Angel Gabriel scratched his head and asked the Lord instead
'What can we do call a land so mean, Sire?'
'Och, Gabe, call it what ye will, maybe Largs or Motherwell,
No, on second thoughts we'll call it Aberdeenshire'

Now there was me and Auntie Annie, Cousin Jock and dear old Granny
And we'd all had a roll in the heather
'Cos we come from Braemar, and we'll not forget that our
Family motto is 'We're all queers together'

Now the old goat died around Eastertide
So Jock rammed the bloody coal scuttle up her
He threw her on the boil, then he topped her off with soil
And served her up as a haggis supper

When a visiting rugby team took a whore from Aberdeen
To agree on a price took an eternity
But she took them without fuss and had triplets on the bus
And sued them for collective paternity

Now wee Ronnie teaches pipes to girls of different types
His methods are a revelation
Just cut your bloody banter, get your mouth around my chanter
And I'll complete your education

Now in Burn's magic prose, a Scottish girl is like a rose
My lass was more like Ben Nevis when I found her
Her southern slopes were grey, half the nation knew the way
And the boys had rammed it up her

MY SISTER LILY

Soloist:

Oh, my sister Lily is a whore in Piccadilly
And my mother is another in the Strand
My father flogs his arsehole round the Elephant and Castle
We're the finest fucking family in the land

All:

Oh, her name is diamond Lily
She's a whore in Piccadilly
And her mother has a brothel in the Strand
Her father sells his arsehole
At the Elephant and Castle
They're the richest fucking family in the land

Soloist:

There's a man deep in a dungeon, with his hand upon his truncheon
And the shadow of his prick upon the wall
And the ladies as they pass, stick their hat-pins up his arse
And the little mice play billiards with his balls

All Chorus

There's a little green urinal, to the north of Waterloo
And another a little further up
There's a member of our school, playing tunes upon his tool
While the passers-by put pennies in his cup

Have you met my Uncle Hector, he's a cock-and-ball inspector
At a celebrated English public school
And my brother sells French letters and a patent cure for wetters
We're not the best of families, ain't it cool?

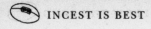

INCEST IS BEST

(to the tune of *Tie Your Kangaroo Down...*)

Chorus:
Incest is best, boys
Incest is best – fuck a relative
Incest is best, boys
Incest is boys

Verses:
Give a piece to your niece, boys
Give a piece to your niece – fuck a relative
Give a piece to your niece, boys
Give a piece to your niece, because...

Other verses include:
Put your knob in Uncle Bob, boys
Give a blow job to your bro, girls
Shower your sis with some piss, boys
Shoot some goo on Aunt Sue, boys
My significant other's my brother, girls
Do the bum of your mum, boys
Give a kiss to your sis, boys
Make love to your cousin, boys
I've just had my dad, girls
Put your sis in bliss, boys
Let's fuck Uncle Buck, girls
Rub your palm on your mum, boys

FOLLOW THE BAND

My lover's a mason, a mason, a mason
A very fine mason is he
All day he lays bricks, he lays bricks, he lays bricks
And when he comes home he lays me

Chorus:
Singing drink a little bit, fuck a little bit
Follow the band (Toot, toot)
Follow the band with your tits in your hands
Dance a little bit, fuck a little bit
Follow the band
Follow the band all the way

My lover's a carpenter, carpenter, carpenter
A very fine carpenter is he
All day he bangs nails, bangs nails, bang nails
And when he comes home he bangs me

Other verses include:
Baker/kneads dough/kneads me
Skier/jumps humps/humps me
Jockey/rides horses/rides me
Swimmer/swims laps/laps me
Pianist/fingers keys/fingers me

NICE GIRLS

(to the tune of *All the Nice Girls Love a Sailor*)

All the nice girls love a candle
All the nice girls love a wick
Because there's something about a candle
That reminds them of a prick
Nice and greasy, slips in easy
It's the surest way to joy
It's been up the Queen of Spain
And it's going up again
Syph ahoy, syph ahoy

All the nice boys love a harlot
All the nice boys love a whore
Because there's something about a harlot
That they've never known before
She'll be willing, for a shilling
And she'll pep you up, my boy
But she'll leave you on the rocks
With a bloody good dose of pox
Syph ahoy, syph ahoy

All the parsons love a choir boy
All the parsons love a bum
Because there's something about a choir boy
That would make an angel come
Roll him over, sleep in clover
It's a curate's only joy
And you needn't give a rap
For you'll never catch the clap
Syph ahoy, syph ahoy

KEYHOLE SONG

The party ended early
'Twas only half past nine
And by some stroke of bloody good luck
Her room was next to mine
And so like Christopher Columbus
I started to explore
And took up my position by the keyhole in the door

Oh the keyhole, keyhole, keyhole
The keyhole in the door
I took up my position by the keyhole in the door

She sat down by the fireside
Her lily white tits to warm
With only a nylon chemise on
To hide her naked form

If only she would take it off
What man could ask for more
By God I saw her take it off
Through the keyhole in the door

Oh the keyhole, keyhole, keyhole
The keyhole in the door
By God I saw her take it off
Through the keyhole in the door

With soft and trembling fingers
I opened up the door
With soft and trembling footsteps
I crossed the bedroom floor

And so that no other man could
See what I'd seen before
I stuffed that nylon chemise
Up the keyhole in the door

Oh the keyhole, keyhole, keyhole
The keyhole in the door
I stuffed that nylon chemise up
The keyhole in the door

That night I slept in rapture
And something else beside
Upon her glorious bosom
Had many a glorious ride

That morning when I woke up
My prick was mighty sore
I felt as if I'd stuffed it up
The keyhole in the door

HERPES SONG

(to the tune of *She Loves You*)

I think I've got a dose
And it's not the dripping kind
It's the one that hurts the most
And it makes you fucking blind

Chorus:
I think it's herpes and you know that can be bad
Yeah that herpes, it can make you fucking mad, ooh
I hate it, yeah, yeah, yeah
I hate it, yeah, yeah, yeah
With a dose like that it's very, very sad

I think I've got a dose
And I got it yesterday
I came so very close
To giving it to the maid

I know there's something wrong
'Cos there's blisters on my knob
And the skin's peeling off my dong
And erections make it throb

I'm going to see the quack
'Cos I can't stand the pain
I stuffed it up her crack
But I won't do that again

When the doctor took his knife
I went deeply into shock
What will I tell the wife
He's gone and cut it off

HELLO PENIS

(to the tune of *Sound of Silence*)

Hello penis, my old friend
I've come to play with you again
When those wet dreams come a-creeping
I spurt my seed while I am sleeping
And with your helmet firmly planted in my hand
It will expand
While jerking off in silence

In horny dreams I get a bone
I beat off on cobble stones
Beneath the halo of a street lamp
I see a whore who's getting very damp
For forty pounds in a flash she's on her back
She spreads her crack
And twitches her twat in silence

And the ants came out and played
In the fucking mess I'd made
But in heeding daddy's warning
That mum would find it in the morning
So I rolled out of bed and wiped it up with my shirt
God, what a squirt!
Jerking off in silence

CUCUMBER SONG

(to the tune of *Botany Bay*)

A restless young lady from Phuket
Developed a wonderful trend
To purchase cucumbers for pleasure
'Cos she found they were better than men

Chorus:
So line up for your cucumbers, ladies
They're selling for two bucks apiece
Your frustrated days are all over
'Cos cucumbers never get pissed

In Asia they're eaten with chillis
In England they're put between bread
But in Phuket we use them as teddies
'Cos we know they'll never want head

They'll never leave stains on the mattresses
They're happy to live in the fridge
The loo seat is never left standing
And I've never seen cucumber kids

So watch out you mighty marauders
You're not quite as great as you think
There's no guarantee it will work again
And we can't trade you in when it shrinks

CLEMENTINE

There she stood beside the bar rail
Drinking pink gin for two bits
And the swollen whiskey barrels
Stood in awe beside her tits

Chorus:
I owe my darlin', I owe my darlin'
I owe my darlin' Clementine
Three bent pennies and a nickel
Oh my darlin' Clementine

Eyes of whiskey, lips of water
As she vomits in my beer
Dawns the daylight in her temple
With a fucking warming leer

Repeat chorus

Hung me guitar on the bar rail
At the sweetness of the sign
In one leap leapt out me trousers
Plunged into the foaming brine

She was bawdy, she was busty
She could match the great Buzoom
As she strained out of her bloomers
Like a melon tree in bloom

Oh the oak tree and the cypress
Never more together twine
Since that creeping poison ivy
Laid its blight on Clementine

CHRISTOPHER ROBIN

(to the tune of *Christopher Robin is Saying His Prayers*)

Little boy kneels at the foot of the stairs
Clutched in his hands are a bunch of white hairs
Oh my, just fancy that
Christopher Robin has castrated the cat

Little boy kneels at the foot of his bed
Lily-white hands are caressing his head
Oh my, couldn't be worse
Christopher Robin is fucking his nurse

Little boys sits on the lavatory pan
Gently caressing his little old man
Flip, flop, into the tank
Christopher Robin is having a wank

FUCK THE GIANT PENIS

(to the tune of *Puff the Magic Dragon*)

Once a pure white virgin lived by the sea
She frolicked over pastoral fields, her name Virginity
A sweet young lass of just sixteen
A rosebud ripe and firm
She wandered o'er the verdant hills
Not knowing of the sperm

Well, Fuck the Giant Penis lived not far away
His cock was damn near two feet long, he poked one twice a day
He was an Ivy Leaguer, with vest and pinstriped shirt
He drove a Roadster XKE, that sexed-up extrovert

One day while he was roaming round the rural strips
He spied her picking flowers there – that bitch with swinging hips
He jumped out of the driver's seat and grabbed her by the arse
He tore off all her clothing and laid her on the grass

Her maiden head was busted, the ground ran bloody red
He poked her till the twilight came, then took her home to bed
He poked her till the sun rose, she begged for more and more
He turned that pure white virgin into a filthy whore

FONDLE ME WITH CARE

(to the tune of *Handle Me With Care*)

I've been sucked off and I've been struck down
I've been pulled off and I've been pulled around
But you're the best fuck that I've ever found
Fondle me with care

Chorus:
I'm so tired of feeling horny
I still have some cum to give
Won't you show me all your pubic hairs
Everybody wants somebody to cream on
Put your body next to mine and dream on

I've had it thin and I've had it thick
I've had my lumps and I've had my licks
But when you play with my prick
Fondle me with care

I've got big, red bloodshot eyes
We stayed up and drank all night
When I exposed myself to your wife
She fondled me with care

Well I flashed my dick and terrorized
Put my tongue between your thighs
Bend over baby and I'll sodomize
Fondle me with care

Well, my balls are tight and I've made a mess
I'll have to clean up my act I guess
Let me put my hand up your dress
And fondle me with care

FIRST ·TIME

The sky was blue
The sun was high
We were alone
Just she and I
Her hair was brown
Her body fine
I ran my hand along her spine
With some courage
I did my best
I placed my hand upon her breast
My other hand shook
As did my heart
I gently spread her legs apart
I knew she was ready
But I didn't know how
It was the first time
I milked a cow

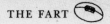

THE FART

(to the tune of *Mademoiselle from Armentières*)

There was an old lady of eighty-two, parlez-vous
There was an old lady of eighty-two, parlez-vous
There was an old lady of eighty-two
Did a fart but missed the loo, inky, pinky, parlez-vous

The fart went rolling down the street, parlez-vous
The fart went rolling down the street, parlez-vous
The fart went rolling down the street
Knocked a copper right off his feet, inky, pinky parlez-vous

The copper got out his rusty pistol, parlez-vous
The copper got out his rusty pistol, parlez-vous
The copper got out his rusty pistol
Shot the fart from here to Bristol, inky, pinky, parlez-vous

Bristol Rovers playing at home, parlez-vous
Bristol Rovers playing at home, parlez-vous
Bristol Rovers playing at home
Kicked the fart from here to Rome, inky, pinky, parlez-vous

Julius Caesar drinking gin, parlez-vous
Julius Caesar drinking gin, parlez-vous
Julius Caesar drinking gin
Opened his gob and the fart went in, inky, pinky, parlez-vous

The fart went rolling down his spine, parlez-vous
The fart went rolling down his spine, parlez-vous
The fart went rolling down his spine
Knocked his bollocks right out of line, inky, pinky, parlez-vous

DUREX IS A GIRL'S BEST FRIEND

(to the tune of *Diamonds are a Girl's Best Friend*)

A poke with a bloke may be quite incidental
Durex is a girl's best friend
You may get the works
But you won't be parental
As he slides it in
You trust that good old latex skin
As he lets fly, none gets by
'Cos it's all gathered up in the end
This little precaution
Avoids an abortion
Durex is a girl's best friend

DO YOUR BALLS HANG LOW?

(to the tune of *Sailor's Hornpipe*)

Do your balls hang low?
Do they swing to and fro?
Can you tie 'em in a knot?
Can you tie 'em in a bow?
Can you throw them o'er your shoulder*
Like a continental soldier?*
Can you do the double shuffle
When your balls hang low?

Chorus:
Ting-a-ling, God damn
Find a woman if you can
If you can't find a woman
Find a clean old man
If you're ever in Gibraltar
Take a flying fuck at Walter
Can you do the double shuffle
When your balls hang low

* *additional verses for lines 5 and 6*

Do they make lusty clamour
When you hit them with a hammer?

Can you bounce 'em off a wall
Like an Indian rubber ball?

Do they have a hollow sound
When you drag 'em on the ground

Do they have a mellow tingle
When you hit 'em with a shingle?

Do they chime like a gong
When you pull upon your dong?

Do they have a salty taste
When you wrap 'em round your waist?

DRUNKEN SAILOR

What shall we do with the drunken sailor
What shall we do with the drunken sailor
What shall we do with the drunken sailor
Earlye in the morning?

Chorus:
Way, hey and up she rises
Way, hey and up she rises
Way, hey and up she rises
Earlye in the morning

Put him into bed with the captain's daughter
(*repeat 3 times*)
Earlye in the morning?

Hang him by the balls in a running bowline (x 3)
Earlye in the morning?

Shave his crotch with a rusty razor (x 3)
Earlye in the morning?

Shove a hosepipe up his arsehole (x 3)
Earlye in the morning?

Tie his prick in a double half-hitch (x 3)
Earlye in the morning

That's what we'll do with the drunken sailor (x 3)
Early in the morning

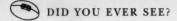

DID YOU EVER SEE?

Oh, I got an Aunt Sissy
And she's only got one titty
But it's very long and pointed
And the nipple's double jointed

Chorus:
Did you ever see
Did you ever see
Did you ever see
Such a funny thing before

I've got a cousin Daniel
And he's got a cocker spaniel
If you tickled him in the middle
He would lift his leg and piddle

Oh, I've got a cousin Rupert
He plays outside-half for Newport
They think so much about him
That they always play without him

Oh, I've got a cousin Anna
And she's got a grand piana
And she'd 'ammer, 'ammer, 'ammer
Till the neighbours say 'God damn her'

Oh I've got a brother Mike
Who rides a motorbike
He can get from here to Gower
In a quarter of an hour

DEAD WHORE

(to the tune of *'My Bonnie lies over the ocean'*)

I passed a dead whore on the roadside
I knew right away she was dead
For the skin on her stomach was flaking
She hadn't a hair on her head
She hadn't a hair on her head

Chorus:
Bring back, bring back
Oh bring back my dead whore to me
Bring back, bring back
Oh bring back my dead whore to me

I first met my dead whore at Mitch's
With a horrible snail-sucking face
She'd roll them around on her tongue
And barf them back up in your face
And barf them back up in your face

Repeat chorus

My dead whore looked into a gas tank
The contents of it for to see
I lit a match to assist her
Oh bring back my dead whore to me
Oh bring back my dead whore to me

While nibbling my dead whore's festered nipples
A horrible thing to discuss
I thought it was milk I was sucking
But it turned out it was syphilitic pus, green pus
But it turned out it was syphilitic pus

My dead whore's vagina was swelling
A condition I thought would soon pass
I stuck in my pecker to explore it
And she farted green gas from her arse
And she farted green gas from her arse

I thought of a way of preserving
My dead whore for posterity
I'd dry her like a piece of beef jerky
With a leathery twat just for me, for me
With a leathery twat just for me

I French-kissed my dead whore named Merly
I thought she had a very active tongue
But after an evening of kissing
I realized it was maggots from her lung
I realized it was maggots from her lung

Once upon thinking it over
I realized my terrible sin
So I stuck my lips on her sweet pussy
And sucked out the load I shot in, shot in
And sucked out the load I shot in

But before I could extract that jism
My dead whore was pregnant and more
Inside the maternity morgue
She gave birth to a dead baby whore
She gave birth to a dead baby whore

DINAH

Chorus:
Dinah, Dinah show us your leg
Show us your leg, show us your leg
Dinah, Dinah show us your leg
A yard above your knee

I wish I were a diamond ring
On Dinah's dainty hand
Then every time she wiped her arse
I'd see the promised land, land, land

The rich girl rides a limousine
The poor girl rides a truck
But the ride that Dinah has
Is when she had a fuck, fuck, fuck

The rich girl uses a sanitary towel
The poor girl uses a sheet
But Dinah uses nothing at all
Leaves a trail along the street, street, street

The rich girl wears a ring of gold
The poor girl one of brass
But the only ring that Dinah wears
Is the one around her arse, arse, arse

The rich girl wears a brassiere
The poor girl uses string
But Dinah uses nothing at all
She lets the bastards swing, swing, swing

The rich girl uses Vaseline
The poor girl uses lard
But Dinah uses axle grease
Because her cunt's so hard, hard, hard

The rich girls work in factories
The poor girls work in stores
But Dinah works in a honky-tonk
With forty other whores, whores, whores

RAWHIDE

Rollin', rollin', rollin'
My dick is getting swollin'
I got this doggie rollin', Rawhide
My knob is hard as leather
But I'll get it in whatever
I wish I could get the tip inside
I stab but I keep missin'
This wasn't made for pissin'
I'm waiting for the first year's ride

Chorus:
Pull 'em down, get 'em off
Get 'em off, pull 'em down
Pull 'em down, get 'em off, Rawhide
Stick it in, pull it out, Rawhide
Pull it out, stick it in
Stick it in, pull it out, Rawhide

She's movin' movin' movin'
Stops my manhood groovin'
This doggie won't stop movin', Rawhide
It's gonna be sore later
But I've been a masturbator
All those years that I've spent inside
My balls they are aching
From ages wanking, waiting
Waiting to get this thing inside

Rollin' rollin' rollin
I'm rootin her assholin'
We're mounted doggie style, Rawhide
I don't try to understand her
Just catch, and grope and bang her
Now her twat is gettin' wet and wide
My forskin's torn and tattered
Her pussy's worn and battered
At last I'll drop my load inside

SWING LOW SWEET CHARIOT

Swing low sweet chariot
Coming forth to carry me home
Swing low, sweet chariot
Coming forth to carry me home

I looked over Jordan and
What did I see
Coming forth to carry me home?
A band of angels coming after me
Coming forth to carry me home

Swing Low etc

If you get there before I do
Coming forth to carry me home
Tell all my friends I'm coming too
Coming forth to carry me home

Swing low, sweet chariot
Coming forth to carry me home
Sometimes I'm up
Sometimes I'm down
Coming forth to carry me home

Yet still my soul feels heavenly bound
Coming forth to carry me home

Swing low etc

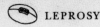

LEPROSY

(to the tune of *Yesterday*)

Birth control, is the only way to save your soul
Since I put it in my girlfriend's hole
Now I believe in birth control

Chorus:
Why I had to come
I don't know she wouldn't blow
I did something wrong
Now I long for birth control

Pregnancy, there's a shotgun hanging over me
Why has this bulge got to be
I should have used one, silly me

Syphilis, feels like razors every time I piss
Who the hell's to blame for this
It's agony this syphilis

Leprosy, bits and pieces falling off of me
I'm not half the man I used to be
Since I acquired leprosy

LET ME BALL YOU SWEETHEART

(to the tune of *Let Me All You Sweetheart*)

Let me ball you sweetheart; I'm in bed with you
Let me hear you whisper that it's time to screw
Make your body wiggle in the same old way
And I'll be back to see you on my next pay day

Let me call you sweetheart; I'm in bed with you
Let me pinch your boobies till they're black and blue
Let me stroke your vulva till it's filled with goo
Let's play hide the weenie up your old wazoo

LITTLE BROWN MOUSE

Oh, the liquor was spilled on the bar room floor
And the place was closed for the night
When out from his hole crept a little brown mouse
And sat in the pale moonlight

Oh, he lapped up the liquor on the bar room floor
And back on his haunches he sat
And all night long you could hear him roar
'BRING ON THE GODDAMNED CAT!'

Oh, and the cat came out and they had a mighty spat
And the cat ate up the mouse
And the moral of the story is
YOU CAN'T DRINK LIQUOR ON THE HOUSE

LULU

(to the tune of *Good Night, Ladies*)

Chorus:
Bang, bang, Lulu
Lulu's gone away
Who's gonna bang, bang
When Lulu's gone away?

Lulu had a baby
It was an awful shock
She couldn't call it Lulu
'Cos the bastard had a cock

I took her to the pictures
We sat down in the stalls
And every time the lights went out
She'd grab me by the balls

She and I went fishing
In a dainty punt
And every time she caught a sprat
She'd shove it up her cunt

Lulu had two boyfriends
Both were very rich
One was the son of a banker
The other the son of a bitch

Lulu had a boyfriend
His name was Tommy Tucker
He took her down the alley
To see if he could fuck her

Lulu was a pretty girl
She had a lot of class
Mini-skirts she'd wear a lot
To let her show her arse

Lulu had a cousin
A stunted little runt
One day they went to have a walk
And he disappeared up her cunt

Lulu had a little lamb
She kept it in a bucket
And every time the lamb jumped out
The bulldog tried to fuck it

Lulu made some porridge
It was very thick
Lulu wouldn't eat it
But she'd smear it on my dick

Lulu had a bicycle
The seat was very blunt
Every time she jumps on it
It sticks her up the cunt

Lulu had a turtle
She also had a duck
She'd put them in the bathtub
To see if they would fuck

Lulu had a job
But then she had to quit
'Cos every time she turned round
The boss would grab her tits

LITTLE BIT OFF THE TOP

(to the tune of *When Johnny Comes Marching Home*)

When I was eight days old, my boys
Hurrah, hurrah
When I was eight days old, my boys
Hurrah, hurrah
The rabbi came with a big, sharp knife
And I surely thought he would take my life
But all he took was a
Little bit off the top

Oh, this is what they call a bris
Hurrah, hurrah
O, this is what they call a bris
Hurrah, hurrah
And if the rabbi doesn't miss
It makes for a much more interesting piss
But all he took was a
Little bit off the top

The rabbi he is called a moyl
Hurrah, hurrah
The rabbi he is called a moyl
Hurrah, hurrah
And over me he sure did toil
I thought I would end up in a goil
But all he took was a
Little bit off the top

Oh, circumcision is all right
Hurrah, hurrah
Oh, circumcision is all right
Hurrah, hurrah
But every morning and every night
You aim to the left and piss to the right
But all he took was a
Little bit of the top

LITTLE RED TRAIN

(to the tune of *When Johnny Comes Marching Home*)

A little red train came down the track
She blew, she blew
A little red train came down the track
She blew, she blew
A little red train came down the track
And I don't give a damn if she never came back
Away she blew, oh Jesus, how she blew

The engineer was at the throttle ... *etc*
A-tossing off in a whisky bottle

The fireman he was shovelling coal ... *etc*
Right up the engineer's arsehole

The switchman he was at the switch ... *etc*
A-swishing away like a son of a bitch

A blonde was in the dining car ... *etc*
A-puffing on a black cigar

A porter was waiting in the car ... *etc*
To take the place of the black cigar

The flagman he stood out on the grass ... *etc*
The staff of the flag ran up his arse

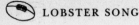

LOBSTER SONG

Oh, Mister fisherman, home from sea
Have you got a lobster you will sell to me?

Chorus:
Singing a-tiddly-a, shit or bust
Never let your bollocks dangle in the dust

Yes sir, yes sir, I have two
And the biggest of the bastards I will sell to you

So I took the lobster home, but I couldn't find a dish
So I put the fucking lobster where the missus has a piss

In the middle of the night, as you well know
The missus got up to let the water flow

Well, first there came a groan, and then there came a grunt
And the bloody big lobster grabbed her by the cunt

The missus grabbed the brush and I grabbed the broom
And we chased the fucking lobster round and round the room

We hit it on the head, we hit it on the side
We hit that fucking lobster till the bastard died

Oh, the story has a moral and this is it
Always have a look before you take a piss

That's the end of my story, there isn't anymore
There's an apple up my arsehole and you can have the core

LOOPY

'Twas down in cunt valley where red rivers flow
Where cocksuckers flourish and maidenheads grow
'Twas there I met Loopy, the girl I adore
She's a hot fucking, cocksucking Mexican whore

Chorus:
She'll fuck you, she'll suck you, she'll tickle your nuts
And if you're not happy, she'll suck out your guts
She'll wrap her legs around you till you want to die
But I'd rather eat Loopy than sweet cherry pie

When Loopy was a young girl of just about eight
She'd swing to and fro on the back garden gate
The crossmember parted, the upright went in
And ever since then she's lived in a welter of sin

Repeat chorus

Now Loopy is dead and she lays in her tomb
The worms crawl around in her decomposed womb
The smile on her face, well it says give me more
I'm a hot fucking, cocksucking, Mexican whore

ON TOP OF OLD SOPHIE

On top of old Sophie
All covered in sweat
I've used fourteen rubbers
But she hasn't come yet

For fucking's a pleasure
And farting's relief
But a long-winded lover
Will bring nothing but grief

She'll kiss you and hug you
Say it won't take too long
But two hours later
You're still going strong

So come all you lovers
And listen to me
Don't waste your erection
On a long-winded she

For your root will just wither
And your passion will die
And she will forsake you
And you'll never know why

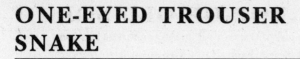

ONE-EYED TROUSER SNAKE

Oh, I've got a little creature
I suppose you'd call him a pet
And if there's something wrong with him
I don't have to see a vet

He goes everywhere that I go
Whether sleeping or awake
God help me if I ever lost
My one-eyed trouser snake

Chorus:
Oh, my one-eyed trouser snake
Oh, my one-eyed trouser snake
God help me if I ever lost
My one-eyed trouser snake

One day I got reading in an old sky pilot's book
About two straker bastards who made the hood go crook
They reckoned it was a serpent that made Eve the apple take
Cripes, that was no fucking serpent, 'twas Adam's one-eyed
trouser snake

I met this arty Sheila who I'd never met before
And something kind of told me she banged like a dunny door
I said 'Come up and see me etching,' she said, 'I hope it's not a
fake'
I said 'It's real, and a work of art. It's my one-eyed trouser
snake'

So come all you little Sheilas and listen to me some
The moral of the trouser snake is short as it is long
Beware of imitation, don't lock your bedroom door
When my pyjama python bites you, you'll be screaming out for
more.

OR WOULD YOU RATHER BE A –?

(to the tune of *Swinging on a Star*)

A pom is an animal that drinks warm beer
He winces at everything he hears
He wears a bowler and eats fish and chips
He never showers and he stinks like shit
So if you're dirty and smelling kind of strong
You could grow up to be a Pom

Chorus:
Or would rather prop up a bar?
Drinking Singhas out of a jar?
And be better of than you are?
Or would you rather be a ?

A yank is an animal that don't know jack shit
He's got no humour and no wit
His beer's like water and he talks too much
He don't even know that a fanny's a crutch
So if you can't tell a jack-off from a wank
You could grow up to be a Yank

An ocker is an animal with corks in his hat
He'd rather drink piss than tickle a twat
He's got a roo for a rabbit and a dingo for a dog
He wishes he could think but he's missing a cog
So if you're dumb and your manners are a shocker
You could grow up to be an Ocker

A kiwi is an animal that likes to fuck sheep
He's so thick it makes you want to weep
He's so damn lazy that he lives on the dole
He'd like to screw women but he can't find their hole
So if you can't tell a ewe from a she
You could grow up to be a Kiwi.

OU EST LE PAPIER?

(to the tune of *Marseillaises*)

A Frenchman went to the lavatory
To have him a jolly good shit
He took his coat and trousers off
So that he could revel in it
But when he reached for the paper
He found that someone had been there before
Ou est le papier?
Ou est le papier?
Monsieur, monsieur, J'ai fait manure
Ou est le papier?

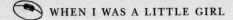

WHEN I WAS A LITTLE GIRL

(to the tune of *Happy Wanderer*)

When I was a little girl, I had a little thing
And if I tried, I could get my little finger in
Finger in, finger in, finger in
Finger iiiiiiiiiiiiiiiiiiii finger in, finger in
My little finger in

I've grown into a woman now, my thing has lost its charm
And I can get five fingers in, and half my fucking arm

Fucking arm, fucking arm, fucking arm
Fucking, aaaaaaaaaaaaaaaaaaaaaaaaaaa fucking arm, fucking arm
And half my fucking arm

Now my age is 92, and I'm half fucking dead
Now I can get both arms in and half my fucking head

Fucking head, fucking head, fucking head
Fucking, eeeeeeeeeeeeeeeeeeeeeeee fucking head, fucking head
And half my fucking head

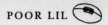

POOR LIL

Her name was Lil and she was a beauty
She came from a house of ill reputy
But she drank too deep of the demon rum
And smoked hashish and opium

She was young and she was fair
She had lovely golden hair
Gentlemen came from miles to see
Lilian in her *deshabille*

Day by day she grew thinner
From insufficient protein in her
She grew two hollows in her chest
Why, she had to go round completely undressed

Now clothes may make a girl go far
But they have no place on a *fille de joie*
Lilian's troubles started when
She concealed her abdomen

She went to the house physician
To presribe for her condition
'You have got,' the doc did say
'Pernicious anem-i-a'

She took to treatment in the sun
She drank of Scotts Emul-si-on
Three times of daily she took yeast
But still her clientele decreased

For you must know her clientel-le
Rested chiefly on her belly
She rilled that thing like the deep Pacific
It was something calorific

As Lilian lay in her dishonour
She felt the hand of the Lord upon her
She said 'My sins I now repent
But Lord, that'll cost you fifty cents'

This is the story of Lilian
She was one girl in a million
This is the moral for her sins
Whatever your line of business –
Fitness wins

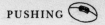

PUSHING

Question:
Was it you that did the pushing?
Left the stains upon the cushion?
Footprints on the dashboard upside down?
Was it you, you sly woodpecker
Who did it to my girl Rebecca?
It was you you'd better leave this town

Answer:
Yes 'twas I that did the pushing
Left the stains upon the cushion
Footprints on the dashboard upside down?
But ever since I had your daughter
I've had trouble passing water
Which makes us kind of even all round

WHILE THE KIWIS SHAGGED

(to the tune of *While Shepherds watched...*)

While the Kiwis shagged their flocks by night
All laying on the ground
Up jumped the Aussie doctor and said
'Stop that and I'll buy a round'

'Fear not' they said
For fear of AIDS had seized the doctor's mind
'Before we Kiwis take a new bride
We clean her out from behind'

So the girls waiting for the question popped
You won't get very far
If you want to take a Kiwi mate
You'll have to answer 'BAAAA'

YELLOW DUMPER TRUCK

(to the tune of *Yellow Submarine*)

In the town where I was born
Lived a man who roamed the land
And he told us of his life, in the back of dumper trucks
So we ran up to the sun, till we found the land of trucks
And we lived a life of sleaze in our yellow dumper truck

Chorus:
We all live in a yellow dumper truck
Yellow dumper truck
Yellow dumper truck
We all live in a yellow dumper truck
Yellow dumper truck
Yellow dumper truck

Most of my friends are all abroad
Many more of them party next door
And the boys begin to chant

Repeat chorus

As we live a life of sleaze
Every one of us has all we need
Plenty of beer and lots of fucks
In our yellow dumper trucks

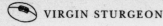

VIRGIN STURGEON

(to the tune of *Reuben and Rachel*)

Chorus:
Cavier comes from the virgin sturgeon
The virgin sturgeon is a very fine fish
The virgin sturgeon needs no urging
That's why cavier is my dish

I gave cavier to my girlfriend
She's a virgin through and through
Since I gave my girlfriend cavier
There ain't nothing she won't do

I gave cavier to my bow-wow
All the other doggies looked agog
He had what those bitches needed
Wasn't he a lucky dog?

I gave cavier to my grandpa
Grandpa's age is ninety-three
Last time that I saw Grandpa
He's chased Grandma up a tree

My father was a lighthouse keeper
He had cavier for his tea
He had three children by a mermaid
Two were kippers, one was me

VLAD

Eat, bite, fuck, suck, gobble, nibble, chew, nipple, bosom,
hair-pie, finger fuck, screw, moose, piss, cat pud, orangutan shit,
sheep pussy, camel crack, pig lie in shit

AW VLAD, AW VLAD

Well, I went to a party and what did they do?
They took off their socks and they took off their shoes
They took off their shirts and they took off their pants
I had a hunch we weren't gonna dance

Everybody's arse was bare
No broads left, just a queer over there
But the whole thing didn't phase me a bit
I just jumped on the pile and grabbed some tit

May baby's not a sports fan,
But she plays with balls whenever she can
'Cos her favourite sport you see
Is playing tonsil tennis with me

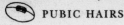

PUBIC HAIRS

(to the tune of *Baby Face*)

Pubic hairs
You've got the cutest little pubic hairs
There's nothing that can compare
Pubic hairs
Penis or vagina, there's nothing that could be finer
Pubic hairs
I'm up in heaven when I'm in your underwear
I don't need a shovel to take a mouthful of
Your cute little pubic hairs

PORTIONS OF A WOMAN

Now the portions of a woman
That appeal to a man's depravity
Are fashioned with the most exquisite care
And that what may seem to you
To be a simple cavity
Is a really an elaborate affair

Now, we doctor's who have taken time
To study these phemonema
In numbers of experimental dames
Have made a little list
Of all these feminine abdomena
And given them delightful Latin names

There's the vulva, the vagina
And the jolly perineum
And the hymen which is sometimes found in brides
And lots of other gadgets
You would love them if you could see 'em
There's the clitoris and Christ knows what else besides

Now it makes us rather tired
When you idle people
Chatter about things to which we've just referred
And to hear you give a name
To such a complicated matter
With such a short and unattractive word – CUNT!

HALLELUJAH, I'M A BUM

Oh why don't you work like other men do?
How the hell can I work when there's nothing to do?

Chorus:
Hallelujah, I'm a bum
Hallelujah, bum, again
Hallelujah to give us a handout
To revive us again

Springtime is here and I'm just out of jail
The whole winter in without any tail

I went to a house and I knocked on the door
My cock sticking straight out and my balls on the floor

I asked for a piece of bread and some food
The lady said 'Bum, you will eat when I'm screwed'

When I left that lady, my cock it was sore
My belly was full, her arse it was tore

I went to another and asked her for bread
She emptied the piss-pot all over my head

Be happy and glad for the springtime has come
We'll throw down our shovels and go on the bum

YOUR LEGS ROUND MY SHOULDERS (FOR HIM)

(to the tune of *Put Your Head on My Shoulders*)

Put your legs around my shoulders (shoulders)
Let me lick your lips slowly (slowly)
You know you are the one and only (only)
Boy, I like it when you sit on my face (my face)

Put your lips on my sweet meat (sweet meat)
'Cos you know that it is a real treat (real treat)
And you know you just can't beat (can't beat)
The taste of my meat in your mouth (your mouth)

Put your legs around my midriff (midriff)
'Cos I've got something really stiff (really stiff)
And I know you'd be really miffed (really miffed)
If you miss out on your chance (EAT SHIT)

YOUR LEGS ROUND MY SHOULDERS (FOR HER)

(to the tune of *Put Your Head on My Shoulders*)

Put your legs round my shoulders (shoulders)
Let me suck your cock slowly (slowly)
Because you know you're not the only (only)
Guy I let sit on my face (face)

Put your lips on my sweet lips (sweet lips)
Let your tongue do the walkin' (walkin')
I'll be doing all the talkin' (talkin')
While I sit on your face (your face)

Put your legs around my midriff (midriff)
Let me ride something real stiff (real stiff)
You know you will be real miffed (real miffed)
If you miss out on the ride of your life (your life)

Turn me round to the other side (other side)
For a different sort of fun ride (fun ride)
You know you won't slip and slide (slip and slide)
When I've got you up on you backside (back side)

Put your lips around my big toe (big toe)
Suck me into erotic throes (erotic throes)
But you really, really must know (must know)
I don't get off on you sucking my big toe (big toe)

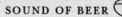

SOUND OF BEER

(to the tune of *Do, Re, Mi*)

Give (*player's name*) a beer, a really big beer
We will watch him drink it down
Girls, you know if he drinks it all
He will never get it up
Oh, the stories sad to tell
It picked up and then it fell
You would die if you could see
(*player's name*) slap his tiny wee-wee

ZOOLOGICAL GARDENS

Thunderin' Jesus it's a lark
In Dublin City after dark
When you're up on a bird in Phoenix Park
Down by the zoological gardens

Last Sunday night we had no dough
So I took the bird up to see the zoo
We saw the lions and the kangaroos
Inside the zoological gardens

Well we went out there by Castlelknock
Said the bird to me 'Sure, we'll court by the lough'
Then I knew she was one of the rare old stock
Inside the zoological gardens

Said the bird to me 'My dear friend Jack
Sure I'd like a ride on the elephant's back'
'If you don't get out of that I'll give you such a crack'
Inside the zoological gardens

We went out there on our honeymoon
Said the bird to me 'If you don't come soon
I'll have to sleep with the hairy baboon'
Inside the zoological gardens

YANK MY DOODLE

Yank my doodle it's a dandy
Yank my doodle till I die
Make that pecker shoot some fireworks
Just like the fourth of July

I've got a Yankee doodle boner
I've had it since you rubbed my thigh
So yank my doodle if you please
That bulge is not a pony
Just stick your fingers up my arse
And stroke my macaroni

Yank my doodle it's so big
Clearly it's a dandy
Stick that sucker in your mouth
You'll swear it tastes like candy

Yank my doodle it's a dandy
Yank my doodle till I die
Lick that lizard till it's standing tall
Right through my pubic hair
If you like Yankee doodle peckers
I've got one that I can spare

So yank my doodle till it comes
Just point it towards your titties
They say that stuff is beauty cream
Let's make your titties pretty

Yank my doodle it's so big
Baby it's a dandy
Jerk that turk and make it squirt
And keep a Kleenex handy

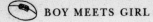

BOY MEETS GIRL

Boy meets girl, holds her hand
Visions of a promised land
Tender words, cling and kiss
Crafty feel, heavenly bliss
Nibble nipples, squeeze thighs
Gets a beat, feels a rise
Eyes ablaze, drawers down
Really starts to go to town
Legs outspread, virgin lass
Fanny foams like bottled Bass
Ram it home, moans of joy
Teenage love, girl meets boy
Love's a jewel, pearls he's won
Shoots his load, what's he done
Comes the payoff, here's the rub
He's got her in the puffing club
Comes the wedding, bridesmaids flap
Love and cherish, all that crap
A tubby tum, weighty gain
Prams and nappies, labour pain
Begins to realize what he did
Nagging wife and screaming kid
Sweats his arse off, works his stint
Only pleasure is evening time
When mattress creaks he's off again
Can't forsake those sexy habits
Breeding kids like bloody rabbits

YOU WON'T FIND ANY COUNTRY

(to the tune of *Wild Rover*)

I've searched the world over, excitement I've sought
But all my experience was dearly bought

Chorus:
So it's no, nay, never
No nay never no more
You won't find any country
Where it pays you to score

To tap a Yank for a good screw, in my belief
Is like asking Mrs Custer to give an Indian relief
In the last year or two they've not used their tush
'Cos they're shagged up the arse by a cowboy called Bush

The Dutch they just sit there, arsehole on bike
One finger up a nostril and one in a dyke
And if they feel chilly when these things they perform
They put their caps up girls' pussies to keep their heads warm

Now haircuts for Germans are four times the price
They charge for each corner and go over it twice
And if you pick up a harlot now don't throw her out
Though her snatch it smells strongly, they just love sauerkraut

The Swiss nation at loving are antiseptic
They put germolene, not Vaseline, on their prick
The Swiss yodel is to cover their sheeps' anguished calls
For their Toblerone pricks make rectangular holes

The Aussies are known for their intake of beer
And they've all been in Sydney, now isn't that queer
To keep flies off from their hat, corks are hung
'Cos a zipper can be painful if caught on the tongue.

VICAR IN THE DOCKSIDE CHURCH

The vicar in the dockside church
One Sunday morning said
'Some dirty bastard's shat himself
I'll punch his fucking head'
Well up jumped Jock from the third row back
And he spat a mighty go-o-b
'I'm the one who shat himself
You can chew my fucking kn-o-b
You can chew my fucking knob'

The organist played *Hearts of Oak*
Mixed up with *Auld Lang Syne*
The preacher then got up and said
'You've had your fucking time'
The organist waltzed down the aisle
With his organ down his back
Then up jumped Jock and hollered out
(And the vicar from his pulp cried)
'You can waltz that bastard ba-a-c-k
You can waltz that bastard back'

Sweet Jenny Lynd got up to sing
She warbled like a thrush
The vicar from his pulpit said
'By God you're fucking lush'
'That's right,' said she 'But I'm not free,
For it's thirty bob a ti-i-me'
Then up jumped Jock and hollered out
(And the vicar from his pulp cried)
'Hand off you bastards she's mi-i-ne
Hands off you bastards she's mine'

161

TEDDY BEAR'S PICNIC

(to the tune of *Teddy Bear's Picnic*)

If you go down to the woods today
You're in for a big surprize
If you go down to the woods today
You'll never believe your eyes
'Cos Mum and Dad are having a screw
Uncle Frank is having a wank
And Auntie D is having it off with Grandad

Those angel bears have come on their bikes
All dressed in their leather gear
There's gallons of scrumps all green with lumps
And horrible Watney's beer
Now one of 'em downed a pint of it quick
And then was promptly horribly sick
And filled up Paddington Bear's new wellies

PISSED

(to the tune of *My Way*)

And now, the beer is near
And so I'll face the golden fluid
My friend, I'll say it clear
Without the beer, I wouldn't be here

I've tried low alcohol beer
But then I've been on every highway
But more, much more than this
I didn't get pissed

Regrets, I've had so many
So then again, back to the real booze
I'll do what men will do
And carry this load on my shoulders

I'll drink each brand of beer
Until I have nothing to fear
But more, much more than this
I like to get pissed

Yes there were times, I'm sure you knew
When I drank more than I should do
But through it all, even be-ing sick
I drank it all and spat it out
I faced the toilet
And I stood tall
And regretted be-ing pissed

I laughed, but then I cried
Because there isn't any beer left
And now, I realize
I didn't find it so amusing

To think, I drank all that
And may I say 'Not in a shy way'
Oh no, oh not me, I want to be pissed

For what is a rugby man
Without a beer
If there is none
Then he stays sober
He'll say the things he truly feels
And not the slime, just to get laid

WOODPECKER'S SONG

I put my finger in a woodpecker's hole
And the woodpecker said 'God bless my soul
Take it out, take it out, take it out
REMOVE IT'

I removed my finger from a woodpecker's hole
And the woodpecker said 'God bless my soul,
Put it back, put it back, put it back,
REPLACE IT'

I replaced my finger in a woodpecker's hole
And the woodpecker said 'God Bless my soul
Turn it round, turn it round, turn it round,
REVOLVE IT'

I revolved my finger in a woodpecker's hole
And the woodpecker said 'God bless my soul
Turn it back, turn it back, turn it back,
REVERSE IT'

I reversed my finger in a woodpecker's hole
And the woodpecker said 'God bless my soul
In and out, in and out, in and out
RECIPROCATE IT'

I reciprocated my finger in a woodpecker's hole
And the woodpecker said 'God bless my soul
Speed it up, speed it up, speed it up
ACCELERATE IT'

I accelerated my finger in a woodpecker's hole
And the woodpecker said 'God bless my soul
Slow it down, slow it down, slow it down,
RETARD IT'

I retarded my finger in a woodpecker's hole
And the woodpecker said 'God bless my soul
Once again, once again, once again
REPEAT IT'

I repeated my finger in a woodpecker's hole
And the woodpecker said 'God bless my soul
Leave it in, leave it in, leave it in
RELAX IT'

I relaxed my finger in a woodpecker's hole
And the woodpecker said 'God bless my soul
Let it go, let it go, let it go
RELEASE IT'

I released my finger in a woodpecker's hole
And the woodpecker said 'God bless my soul
Pull it out, pull it out, pull it out
RETRACT IT'

I retracted my finger in a woodpecker's hole
And the woodpecker said 'God bless my soul
Take a whiff, take a whiff, take a whiff
REVOLTING'

WHEN THE END OF THE MONTH ROLLS AROUND

(to the tune of *Field Artillery Song*)

You can tell by the stain that she's in a lot of pain
When the end of the month rolls around
You can tell by her stance she's got cotton in her pants
When the end of the month rolls around

Chorus:
For it's hi, hi, hee, in the Tampon industry
Shout out your sizes loud and strong
Junior, regular, super-duper, Bale of Hay
For wherever we go you will always know
When the end of the month rolls around

You can tell by her walk that you'll sit around and talk
When the end of the month rolls around
You can tell by the blotch that she's got a leaky crotch
When the end of the month rolls around

You can tell by her eyes there is blood between her thighs
When the end of the month rolls around
You can tell by her pout that her eggs are falling out
When the end of the month rolls around

You can tell by her stance that there's bleeding in her pants
When the end of the month rolls around
You can tell that it itches by the way she always bitches
When the end of the month rolls around

You can bet it ain't sweat when her underwear is wet
When the end of the month rolls around
You can tell by the stink that she isn't in the pink
When the end of the month rolls around

WILL YOU MARRY ME?

If I give you half a crown
Can I take your knickers down
Will you marry, marry, marry, marry, marry, will you marry me?

If you give me half a crown
You can't take my knickers down
You can't marry, marry, marry, marry, marry, you can't marry me?

If I give you two and six
Will you let me squeeze your tits
Will you marry, marry, marry, marry, marry, will you marry me?

If you give me two and six
I won't let you squeeze my tits
You can't marry, marry, marry, marry, marry, you can't marry me?

If I give you my big chest
And all the money I possess
Will you marry, marry, marry, marry, marry, will you marry me?

If you give me your big chest
And all the money you possess
I will marry, marry, marry, marry, marry, I will marry you

Get out of the door you lousy whore
My money was all that you were looking for
And I'll not marry, marry, marry, marry, marry, I 'll not marry you

HARVEST OF LOVE

I rise at six and I feed the chicks
And I'm feeling lonesome and blue
And when I milk the cow it seems somehow
My thoughts keep straying to you
And as the horse and I plough the fields nearby
Your memory I can't erase
'Cos when I walk at the rear of the horse, my dear
I seem to see your face

Chorus:
I'm gonna sow the seeds of deep devotion
Fertilize it with emotion
Water it with warm desire
And then I'll reap the harvest of love

Side by side we'll take a ride
In my horse and buggy one day
Down lover's lane I'll turn the reins
And my horse will run out of hay
And I will kiss those lips, those tempting lips
The only ones that can thrill me
And we will frolic at night in the pale moonlight
If the wife ever finds out she will kill me

THE TINKER

The lady of the manor
Was dressing for the ball
When she spied a Highland tinker
Wanking up against the wall

Chorus:
With his bloody great kidney wiper
And his balls the size of three
And a yard and a half of foreskin
Hanging down below his knee

The lady wrote a letter
And in it she did say
'I'd rather be fucked by you, sir
Than his Lordship any day'

The tinker got the letter
And when it he did read
His balls began to fester
And his prick began to bleed

He mounted on his donkey
And he rode up to the Strand
His balls across his shoulder
And his penis in his hand

He fucked the cook in the kitchen
He fucked the maid in the hall
And then he fucked the butler
The dirtiest trick of all

THE TINKER

And then he fucked the mistress
In ten minutes she was dead
With a yard and a half of foreskin
Hanging round her head

The tinker now is dead, sir
And they say he's gone to Hell
And there he fucks the devil
And I hope he fucks him well

GIVE ME A CLONE

(to the tune of *Home on the Range*)

Oh, give me a clone
Of my own flesh and bone
With its Y-chromosome changed to an X
And when it is grown
Then my own little clone
Will be of the opposite sex

Chorus:
Clone, clone of my own
With its Y-chromosome changed to an X
And when I'm alone
With my own little clone
We will both think of nothing but sex

Oh, give me a clone
Is my sorrowful moan
A clone that is wholly my own
And if she's an X
Of the feminine sex
Oh, what fun we will have when we're prone

My heart's not of stone
As I've frequently shown
When alone with my own little X
And after we've dined
I'm sure we will find
Better incest than Oedipus Rex

Why should such sex vex
Or disturb or perplex
Or induce a disparaging tone
After all, don't you see
Since we're both of us are me
When we're having sex, I'm alone

And after I'm done
She'll still have her fun
For I'll clone myself 'ere I die
And this time without fail
They'll be both of them male
And they'll each ravish her by and by

SOD 'EM ALL

Sod 'em all, Sod 'em all
The long and the short and the tall
Sod all the sergeants and W.O. ones
Sod all the corporals and their bastard sons
For we're saying goodbye to them all
As back to their billets they crawl
You'll get no promotion this side of the ocean
So cheer up my lads, sod 'em all

Sod 'em all, Sod 'em all
The skipper, the jimmy and all
Sod all the yeoman and C.P.O. tels
Sod the chief sloshies and their bleeding smells
For we're saying goodbye to them all
As back to their hammocks they crawl
You'll get no promotion this side of the ocean
So cheer up my lads, sod 'em all

Sod 'em all, Sod 'em all
The jaunty, the crusher and all
Sod all the shipwrights and C.P.O. cooks
Sod all the paybobs with their bleeding books
For we're saying goodbye to them all
As back to their hammocks they crawl
You'll get no promotion this side of the ocean
So cheer up my lads, sod 'em all

Sod 'em all, Sod 'em all
The admiral, the flag-jack and all
Sod all the O.A.s and E.A.s as well
Sod the chief stoker and send him to Hell
For we're saying goodbye to them all
As back to their hammocks they crawl
You'll get no promotion this side of the ocean
So cheer up my lads, sod 'em all

SWEET VIOLETS

(to the tune of *Sweet Violet*)

Chorus:
Sweet violets, sweeter than the roses
Covered all over from head to toe
Covered all over in SHIT, SHIT, SHIT

My father was a coal miner
He worked in a deep, dark pit
Sometimes he'd shovel up coal dust
And other times he'd shovel up shit

My brother was a pilot
And he never wanted to quit
Sometimes he'd land on the runway
And other times he'd land in the shit

My wife, she died on the toilet
She died of a horrible fit
And to satisfy her last wishes
She was buried in six foot of shit

My father went to the woodshed
Some wood he wanted to split
But when he grabbed hold of the handle
He found it was covered in shit

Phyllis Quat kept a sack in the garden
I was curious I must admit
One day I stuck in my finger
And pulled it out covered in shit

I sat in a gold lavatory
In the home of the Baron of Split
The seat was encrusted in rubies
But as usual the bowl contained shit

My brother he worked in a sewer
Some lamps they had to be lit
One evening there was an explosion
And my brother was covered in shit

Phllyis Quat took a bag to her boyfriend's
But the bag it was old and it split
Now the boyfriend and Phyllis have parted
For the bag was packed full of shit

Now the baby was eating an apple
They thought he had swallowed a pip
But when they examined his appy
They found it was covered in shit

Well now my song is ended
And I have finished my bit
And if any of you feel offended
Stick your head in a bucket of shit

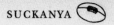

SUCKANYA

(to the tune of *Oh, Diana*)

I'm so young and you're so old
You've had a baby I've been told
I don't care what my friends say
I'll pay your bar fine any day
You and I shall never part
I'll give you five hundred baht
Oh please go down on me, Suckanya

I bought you a house and a brand new car
In the Rock Hard you're a star
You go out late every night
Come home at noon, oh what a sight
In your heart I'll always stay
As long as I can pay, pay, pay
Oh please go down on me, Suckanya

You gave me clap and you wear gold
My motorcycle you have sold
To pay my bills at Adam and Eve
The fruits of love are never free
All I ask is one more suck
But you don't even give a fuck
Oh please go down on me Suckanya

Your Thai husband threw me out
Tell me what's it all about
Now you're into sniffing glue
Does this mean that we are through
I love you with all my heart
So don't cut off my private part
Oh please go down on me Suckanya

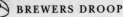

BREWERS DROOP

Once there was a time when we'd fuck all night
Now no more than once a month, no way
I'm always asking for a little extra
But you shy away and say 'Oh, not today'

Chorus:
'Cos you've got brewer's droop
Some girls have all the luck
They get it day and night for weeks on end
But you won't look at me
It's really sad to see
What that brewer's droop has done to me

I used to worry about another woman
Who was taking you away from me
But then I learned the cause of your deflation
Wasn't someone else sat on your knee

So boys as you swig upon that bottle
Please remember what we have to say
If you want to play when you go home horny
Push that one last bottle out of the way

THE 12 DAYS OF RAMADAN

(to the tune of *12 Days of Christmas*)

On the first day of Ramadan King Khalid gave to me:
A book by Salman Rushdie
(*throw to ground and stamp on it*)

Two Yemenese
(*big spit*)

Three Ayatollahs
(*sing 'Ayatollah Ayatollah' while bowing in prayer*)

Four Iraqi mine sweepers
(*put hands over ears and stamp feet*)

Five Iranian terrorists
(*jump forward and spray crowd with machine gun fire*)

Six cruise missiles
(*use hands to simulate rocket travelling through air*)

Seven SAS
(*whistle* Colonel Bogey *tune*)

Eight blindfolded hostages
(*Sing* Show me the way to go home, *while stumbling around with arms outstretched*)

Nine raving mullahs
(*Shout 'Down with Israel, Down with Israel' while shaking fists in the air*)

Ten Scud missiles

(*Fingers in ear and say 'Na, na, na, na, na, you missed me, you missed me'*)

Eleven open sewers
(*Sing 'What pong, what a pong' to the tune of* William Tell *overture*)

Twelve circumcisions
(*Yell 'Ooh that hurts', while running around clutching genitals*)

HANKY PANKY

(to the tune of *Hokey Cokey*)

You give the right eye wink
You give the left eye wink
You do the 'come here' wink
And he buys us both a drink

Chorus:
You do the hanky panky
Get his trousers down
That's what it's all about

You do the top lip lick
You do the bottom lip lick
You give a little giggle
'Cos he thinks you'll suck his prick

Repeat chorus

You put your right tit out
Your left tit out
Nipples getting harder
So you shake them all about

You put your right cheek out
You put your left cheek out
You give a little wobble
Watch his eyes pop out

Your put your right leg out
You put your left leg out
Spread them at the knees
So he can see what it's all about

You put the right hip out
The left hip out
Grab him by the bollocks
And you squeeze till he spouts

You put your pelvis in
You put your pelvis out
Go a little faster
And you grind it all about

You give the right ear groan
You give the left ear groan
Groan a little faster
'Cos he's going to drop his load

You give a right cheek kiss
You give a left cheek kiss
Hate to be a liar
But you tell him it was bliss

We've done the hanky panky
Got his trousers down
So FUCK OFF!

TOASTS

(to the tune of *Recited*)

Here's to the gash that never heals
The more you touch it the better it feels
Rub it and tub it and scrub it like hell
You'll never get rid of that fishy old smell

Here's to the girl who lives on the hill
If she won't do it her sister will
Here's to her sister!

Here's to the breezes
That blow through the trees
And lifts the girls' dresses
Way over their knees
And show us the creases
That twitches and squeezes
And teases and pleases
And carries diseases
By Jesus!

If I had a dog who could piss this stuff (*holding up a beer*)
And if I knew he could piss enough
I'd tie his head to the foot of the bed
And suck his dick till we both dropped dead

Here's to the lady dressed in black
Once she walks by she never looks back
And when she kisses, oh how sweet
She makes things stand that never had feet

185

Here's to me in my sober mood
When I ramble, sit and think
Here's to me in my drunken mood
When I gamble, sin and drink
And when my days are over
And from this world I pass
I hope they bury me upside down
So the world can kiss my arse!

THREE GERMAN OFFICERS

(to the tune of *Mademoiselle from Armentières*)

Three German officers crossed the Rhine
Parlez-vous, parlez-vous?
Three German officers crossed the Rhine
Parlez-vous, parlez-vous?
Three German officers crossed the Rhine
Fucked the women and drank their wine
Inky pinky parlez-vous

They came upon a wayside inn (x3)
Pissed on the mat and walked right in
Inky pinky *etc...*

Oh landlord have you a daughter fair (x3)
With lily-white tits and golden hair *etc...*

Oh yes I have but she's too young (x3)
To sleep with a German stinking Hun *etc...*

Oh father dear I'm not too young (x3)
To sleep with a German stinking Hun *etc...*

Up the rickety stairs they went (x3)
Threw her down upon the bed *etc...*

They tied her to the leg of the bed (x3)
Fucked her till she was nearly dead *etc...*

They took her down a shady lane (x3)
Fucked her back to life again *etc...*

They fucked her up, they fucked her down (x3)
They fucked her right around the town *etc...*

They fucked her in they fucked her out (x3)
They fucked her up the water spout *etc...*

Seven months went and all was well (x3)
Eight months went and she started to swell *etc...*

Nine months on and she gave a grunt (x3)
And a little white bastard popped out of her cunt *etc...*

The little white bastard grew and grew (x3)
He fucked his mother and his sister too *etc...*

The little white bugger he went to Hell (x3)
He fucked the devil and his wife as well *etc...*

HARLOT OF JERUSALEM

In days of old there lived a maid
Who used to do a roaring trade
A prostitute of ill repute
The harlot of Jeruslam

She lived within the palace walls
And round the walls were hung the balls
Of every cock who'd tried to root
The harlot of Jerusalem

Nearby there lived an Arab tall
Who with his prick could move a wall
It was the pride of nearly all
The harlots of Jerusalem

One night returning from a spree
He saw her there beneath a tree
And vowed that very night that he
Would lay her in Jerusalem

He took her to a shady nook
And from his open fly he took
A penis like a butcher's hook
The finest in Jerusalem

He laid her down upon her back
And tried to shove it up her crack
But had no luck in trying to fuck
The harlot of Jerusalem

Cathusalem, she gave a grunt
And with a snap she shut her cunt
And threw him high into the sky
Far beyond Jerusalem

Away he flew across the seas
Across the sea of Galilee
And caught his bollocks in a tree
Three leagues beyond Jerusalem

And there he hangs unto this day
And seen by all who pass his way
The silly ape who tried to rape
The harlot of Jerusalem

ROLL YOUR LEG OVER

(to the tune of *Oh Sally, My Dear*)

If all the young girls were like fish in the ocean
Then I'd be a whale and I'd show them the motion

Chorus:
Oh, roll your leg over
Oh, roll your leg over
Roll your leg over and fuck me till noon

If all the young girls were like fish in a pool
I'd be a shark with a waterproof tool

If all the young girls were like in the brookie
I'd be a trout and I'd get me some nookie

If all the young girls were like winds on the sea
I'd be a snail and I'd have them blow me

If all the young girls were like cows in the pasture
I'd be a bull and I'd fill them with rapture

If all the young girls were like mares in the stable
I'd be a stallion and show them I'm able

If all the young girls were like bricks in a pile
I'd be a mason and lay them in style

If all the young girls were like bells in a tower
I'd be a clapper and bang them each hour

If all the young girls were like bats in a steeple
And I were a bat, there'd be more bats than people

If all the young girls were like little red foxes
And I were a hunter, I'd shoot up their boxes

If all the young girls were like little white rabbits
And I were a hare, I would teach them bad habits

If all the young girls were like trees in the forest
And I were a woodsman, I'd split their clitoris

If all the young girls were like telephone poles
I'd be a squirrel and stuff nuts in their holes

I wish all the girls were like statues of Venus
And I were equipped with a petrified penis

RUB-A-DEE-DUB

(to the tune of *The Scotsman*)

Now the baker's boy to the mart he went
Some pork for him to buy
And when he got upon the spot
No one he could spy
And just as he was about to leave
Thinking all was dead
He heard the sound of a rub-a-dee-dub
Right above his head

Now the baker's boy was cunning and wise
And he crept up the stairs
And he crept up so silently
He caught them unawares
And there he saw the butcher's boy
Between his missus' thighs
And they were having a rub-a-dee-dub
Right before his eyes
Oh, they were having a rub-a-dee-dub
Right before his eyes

Now the butcher's wife was much alarmed
Aleaping from the bed
She turned unto the baker's boy
And this is what she said
'If you were but my secret kept
Just bear this in mind
You can always come for a rub-a-dee-dub
Whenever you feel inclined
Oh, you can always come for a rub-a-dee-dub
Whenever you feel inclined'

Now the baker's boy was filled with joy
At the prospect of such fun
He'd barely leaped upon the bed
When the butcher's boy was done
But when he came to the shortest strokes
How he kissed the butcher's wife
He vowed he'd have a rub-a-dee-dub
Every day of his life
Oh, he vowed he'd have a rub-a-dee-dub
Every day of his life

Now in the morn when he awoke
All over he did quake
His back was sore, his balls were raw
All over he did shake
And when he looked at his Tom-tom
He saw he'd done the trick
The consequence of his rub-a-dee-dub
Were pimples on his prick
Oh, the consequence of his rub-a-dee-dub
Were pimples on his prick

Now the baker's boy to the doctor went
Some ointment for to buy
The doctor looked him up and down
And heaved a mighty sigh
'My boy, my boy,' the doctor said
'You've been a bloody fool
You'll never more have a rub-a-dee-dub
I'm goona cut off your tool
Oh, you'll never more have a rub-a-dee-dub
I'm goona cut off your tool'

Now listen to the baker's boy
For he should surely know
An enthusiastic amateur
Is worse than any pro
And if you would a-wooing go
And self-control you lack
Whenever you have a rub-a-dee-dub
Be sure to wear a mack
Oh, whenever you have a rub-a-dee-dub
Be sure to wear a mack

THERE WAS AN OLD FARMER

There was an old farmer who sat on a rock
Shaking and waving his big, hairy cock
First at the ladies next door at the Ritz
Who taught the young children to play with their tits
Kite strings and marbles and all things galore
Along came a lady who looked like a whore
Decent young lady, but walked like a duck
She thought she'd invented a new way to fuck
Bring up the children to sew and to knit
The boys in the stable were shovelling shit
Litter and paper from yesterday's hunt
And old farmer Potter was having some cunt
Cake in the stable and singing this song
If you think that's dirty
You're fucking well wrong

RINGADANGDOO

(to the tune of *My Ding-a-ling*)

Chorus:
The ringadandoo pray what is that?
It's furry and soft, like a pussy cat
It's got a crack down the middle
And a hole right through
That's what they call the ringadandoo

I once knew a girl, her name was Jean
The sweetest girl I'd ever seen
She loved a boy, who was straight and true
Who longed to play on her ringadandoo

So she took him to her father's house
And crept inside as quiet as a mouse
And they shut the door and the window too
And he played all night on her ringadandoo

The very next day her father said
You've gone and lost your maidenhead
You can pack your bags and your suitcase too
And bugger off with your ringadandoo

So she went to town and became a whore
And hung a red light outside her door
And one by one and two by two
They came to play on her ringadandoo

There came to that town a son of a bitch
Who had the pox and the seven-year itch
He had gonorrhea and syphilis too
So that was the end of her ringadandoo

RAJAH OF AATRAKHAN

There was a Rajah of Aatrakhan
Yo ho, yo ho
A most licentious fucking man
Yo ho, yo ho
Of wives he had a one hundred and nine
Including his favourite concubine
Yo ho, you buggers, yo ho, you buggers
Yo ho, yo ho, yo ho

One day when he had a hell of a stand
He called to a warrior, one of his band
Go down without wasting any time
And bring me my favourite concubine

The warrior fetched the concubine
A face like Venus, a face divine
The Rajah gave a significant grunt
And rammed his penis right up her cunt

The Rajah's cries were loud and long
The maiden's cries were sure and strong
But just when all had come to a head
They both fell through the fucking bed

They hit the floor with a hell of a grunt
Which completely buggered the poor girl's cunt
And as for the Rajah's magnificnet cock
It never recovered from the shock

There is a moral to this tale
There is a moral to this tale
If you would fuck a girl at all
Stand her right up against the wall

THE BRITISH GRENADIER

Some die of constipation
And some of diarrhoea
And some of masturabtion
And some of gonorrhea
But of all the world's diseases
There's nothing can compare
With the drip, drip, drip of the syphilitic prick
Of a British Grenadier

When he goes forth in battle
His weapon in his hand
The lasses fall like cattle
There's none can make a stand
But when the campaign's over
It's then he feels so queer
With the drip, drip, drip of the syphilitic prick
Of a British Grenadier

And when he does retire
To take his well-earned rest
There burns an ancient fire
To do what he does best
And yet the truth is bitter
There's one thing he does fear
It's the drip, drip, drip of the syphilitic prick
Of a British Grenadier

MY OWN GRANDPA

I'm my own Grandpa
I'm my own Grandpa
It sounds funny I know
But it's really so
I'm my own Grandpa

I'm my own Grandpa
I'm my own Grandpa
It sounds funny I know
But it's really so
I'm my own Grandpa

Many years ago
When I was twenty-three
I was married to a widow
Who was pretty as could be
This widow had a grown-up daughter
Who had hair of red
My father fell in love with her
And soon the two were wed

This made my father my son-in-law
Which changed my very life
My daughter was my mother
For she was my father's wife
And to complicate the matter
Even though it brought me joy
I soon became the father
Of a bouncing, baby boy

This little baby, then
Became the brother of my dad
So he became the uncle
Though it made me sad
By then he was my uncle
And he also was the brother
Of the grown-up daughter
Who of course was my step mother

My father's wife then had a son
Who kept them on the run
He just became the grandchild
For he was my daughter's son
My wife is now my father's mother
And it makes me blue
Although she is my wife
She is my grandmother too

Now if my wife is my grandmother
I am her grandchild
And every time I think of it
It really drives me wild
Now I have become the strongest
Case you ever saw
I am the husband of my own grandmother

I'm my own Grandpa
I'm my own Grandpa
It sounds funny I know
But it's really so
I'm my own Grandpa

MY GOD HOW THE MONEY ROLLS IN

(to the tune of *Bonnie Lies Over the Ocean*)

My father makes books on the corner
My mother makes illicit gin
My sister sells kisses to sailors
My God, how the money rolls in

Chorus:
Rolls in, rolls in
My God how the money rolls in
Rolls in, rolls in
My God how the money rolls in

My mother's a bawdy housekeeper
Each night when the evening grows dim
She hangs out a little red lantern
My God, how the money rolls in

My cousin's a Harley Street surgeon
With instruments long, sharp and thin
He only does one operation
My God, how the money rolls in

Uncle Joe is a registered plumber
His business is in holes and in tin
He'll plug up your hole for a tenner
My God, how the money rolls in

My brother's a slum missionary
He saves fallen women from sin
He'll save you a blonde for a dollar
My God how the money rolls in

My Grandad sells cheap prophylactics
He punctures the teats with a pin
For Grandma gets rich from abortions
My God how the money rolls in

My sister's a barmaid in Sydney
For a shilling she'll strip to the skin
She's stripping from morning till midnight
My God how the money rolls in

We've started an old-fashioned gin shop
A regular palace of sin
The principal girl is my Grandma
My God how the money rolls in

WHEN I CAME HOME ON A SATURDAY NIGHT

Chorus:
When I came home on Saturday night
As drunk as I could be
There was a horse in the stable
Where my horse should be

I said to my wife the bane of my life
Now please can you tell me
Now what's that horse in the stable
Where my old horse should be

Ah, you're drunk, you're drunk you silly old fool
As drunk as drunk could be
That's not a horse in the stable
But a milk cow that you see

Well I've been all around this great big world
Ten thousand times or more
But a milk cow without an udder
I've never seen before

Verses:
There was a hat on the hat rack
But a chamber you see –
But a chamber pot with a hat brand

There was a head upon my pillow
But a water melon that you see
But a water melon with a moustache

There was a prick in the hole
But a carrot that you see
But a carrot with cock and balls

There was a cum stain on the window sill
But baby's milk you see
But baby's milk that smells like cum

NICK-NACK PADDY WHACK

(to the tune of *This Old Man*)

This old man, he fucked one
Don't you know he had so much fun

Chorus:
With a nick-nack paddy whack
He fucked his dog alone
Fucked his pooch and made her moan

This old man he fucked two
A baby rabbit and a kangaroo

This old man he fucked three
Put mirrors up so he could see

This old man he fucked four
Three wasn't enough so he bought a whore

This old man he fucked five
Two were dead and three alive

This old man he fucked six
Had his sister turning tricks

This old man he fucked seven
The youngest one was just eleven

This old man he fucked eight
One sucked him raw and it felt great

This old man he fucked nine
God this orgy is divine

This old man he fucked ten
All he could say was 'do it again'

This old man he fucked eleven
Died of VD and went to Heaven

With a nick-nack-paddy-whack
Now his dog's alone
No one left to make her moan

BREATHALYZED

(to the tune of *Yesterday*)

Breathalyzed
Crystals turning green before my eyes
I can hardly realize, that I have been breathalyzed

Suddenly, there's a policeman standing over me
I'd like to punch him but he's six-foot three
And I would like to stay alive

Reality, five hundred milligrammes per hundred mils
Now they reckon, I'm a mobile still
And I have to be penalized

Custody, when they took me to the local nick
I've never seen a policeman move so quick
But not as quick as I got sick

Misery, and the judge says I must join AA
And take the bus for sixty days
Oh, why did I get breathalyzed?

COLOSTOMY'S BEST

(to the tune of *Tie Me Kangaroo Down...*)

Chorus:
Colostomy's best, boys
Colostomy's best – FILL YOUR BAGGIE
Colostomy's best, boys
Colostomy's best, so

Rub some shit on your clit, girls
Rub some shit on your clit – COLOSTOMY
Rub some shit on your clit, girls
Rub some shit on your clit, so

Other verses:
Take a dump in a bag, guys

Shit through a slit in the side, Clyde

Stick your tool in her stool, boys

Get down in her brown, boys

Whack off in her sack, Jack

Fart through a cut in your gut, boys

Make a doo-doo without a loo, Stu

FOGGY DEW

Well, I am a bachelor, I live by myself
I work at the weaver's trade
And the only lowly thing I ever did wrong
Was to woo a fair young maid
And in the winter, too
But the only lowly thing I ever did wrong
Was to keep her from the foggy, foggy dew

One night this maid came up to my bed
Where I lay fast asleep
She laid her head upon my chest
And then began to weep
She sighed, she cried, she damn near died
She said 'What shall I do?'
So I took her to bed and covered her up her head
Just to keep her from the foggy, foggy dew

All through the first part of the night
We did laugh and play
And through the latter part of the night
She slept in my arms till day
Then when the sun shone on our bed
She cried 'I am undone'
'Hold your tongue you silly girl
The foggy, foggy dew is gone'

Now I am a bachelor, I live with my son
I work at the weaver's trade
And every time I look into his face
He reminds me of the fair, young maid
He reminds me of the summer time
And the winter too
And the many, many times I took her in my arms
Just to keep her from the foggy, foggy dew

ONE-EYED RILEY

When I was sitting by the fire
Drinking a whisky, passing water
Suddenly a thought came to my mind
I'd like to fuck O'Reilly's daughter

Chorus:
Giddy-eye-eye, giddy-eye-oh
Giddy-eye-eye, for the one-eyed Riley
Rough 'em up, stuff 'em up, balls and all
Hey jig-a-jig-eye-oh

Her hair was black, her eyes were blue
The Colonel, the Major and the Captain sought her
The regimental goat and the drummer boy too
But they never had a fuck with O'Riley's daughter

Jack O'Flanagan is my name
I'm the king of copulation
Drinking beer is my claim to fame
Fucking women is my occupation

Walking through the town one day
Who should I meet but O'Riley's daughter
Never a word to her did I say
But 'Don't you think we really oughta?'

Up the stairs and into bed
There I cocked my left leg over
Marianne was smiling then
Smiling still when the fuck was over

Fucked her till her tits were flat
Filled her up with soapy water
She won't get away with that
If she doesn't have twins she really oughta

Suddenly footsteps on the stairs
Old man Riley bent on slaughter
Bloody great pistol in his hand
Looking for the one who fucked his daughter

He fired the pistol at my head
Missed me by an inch and a quarter
Hit his daughter Marianne
Right in the place where she passes water

I grabbed O'Riley by the hair
Shoved his head in a bucket of water
Rammed his pistol up his arse
A damn sight quicker than I fucked his daughter

Old man Riley's dead and gone
Shall we bury him? Not fucking likely
We'll nail him to the shithouse door
And there we'll bugger him twice nightly

Come you virgins, maidens fair
Answer me quick and true not slyly
Do you want it straight and square
Or the way I gave it to one-eyed Riley?

PRETTY REDWING

There once was an Indian maid
Who was always afraid
That some buckaroo would slip it up her flue
As she lay sleeping the whole night through

She had an idea grand
And she filled it up with sand
So no big buck in search of a fuck
Could reach the promised land

Oh, the moon shines bright on pretty Redwing
As she lay sleeping
Then came a-creeping
A cowboy he came creeping
His heart a-leaping as he spied her

Redwing sprang to life
And whipped out her bowie knife
With two quick cuts she severed his nuts
And then she stabbed him in the guts

The cowboy he did die
Beneath the prairie sky
He stretched his luck in search of a fuck
For Redwing was too sly

Oh, the moon shines bright on pretty Redwing
As she lies snoring there hangs a warning
The cowboy's balls are now adorning
Her teepee awning for all to see

But to her big surprise
Her belly began to rise
And out of her cunt came a little runt
Who had a strange look in his eyes

Poor Redwing was distressed
Until the chief confessed
You can't pull wool over Sitting Bull
At fucking he's the best

Oh, the moon shines bright on pretty Redwing
Within her teepee her kid makes peepee
And poor Redwing is constantly sleepy
As she makes yipee with Sitting Bull

CHRISTMAS CAROL

(to the tune of *Silent Night*)

Sodomy, masturbate, fellation, copulate
Round the world and the M1 motorway
Fornicating in the hay
These are the tricks that I lo-ve
These are the tricks that I love

Condom, prophylactic
Spermicide does the trick
IUDs and birth control pills
Pull it out and let it spill
These will make it sa-fe
These will make it safe

COLD WINTER'S EVENING

(to the tune of *She was just a Poor Man's Daughter*)

'Twas a cold winter's evening
The guests were all leavin'
O'Leary was closing the bar
When he turned and said
To the lady in red
'Get out! You can't stay where you are'

Oh she wept a sad tear
In her bucket of beer
As she thought of the cold night ahead
When a gentleman dapper
Stepped out of the crapper
And these are the words that he said:

'Her mother never taught her
The things that a young girl should know
About the ways of college men
And how they come and go (mostly go)
Age has stolen her beauty
And sin has left its sad scar (you know where)
So remember your mothers and sisters, boys
And let her sleep under the bar (with old Grandad)'

POOR LITTLE ANGELINE

She was sweet sixteen and the village queen
Pure and innocent was Angeline
A virgin still, never known a thrill
Poor little Angeline

At the village fair, the squire was there
Masturbating in the middle of the square
When he chanced to see the dainty knee
Of poor little Angeline

Now the village squire had a low desire
To be the biggest bastard in the whole damn shire
He had set his heart on the fereal part
Of poor little Angeline

As she lifted her skirt to avoid the dirt
She slipped in the puddle of the squire's last squirt
And his knob grew raw at the sight he saw
Of poor little Angeline

So he raised his hat and said, 'Miss, your cat
Has been run over and is squashed flat
But my car is in the square and I'll take you there
Oh dear little Angeline'

Now the filthy old turd should have got the bird
Instead she followed him without a word
And as they drove away, you could hear them say
Poor little Angeline

They had not gone far when he stopped his car
And took little Angeline into a bar
Where he filled her with gin, just to make her sin
Poor little Angeline

When he'd oiled her well he took her to a dell
And there he gave her merry fucking hell
And he tried his luck with a low down fuck
Oh poor little Angeline

With a cry of 'Rape' he raised his cape
Poor little Angeline had no escape
Now it's time someone came to save the name
Of poor little Angeline

Now the story is told of a blacksmith bold
Who'd loved Angeline for years untold
He was handsome to and promised to be true
To poor little Angeline

But sad to say the very same day
The blacksmith had gone to jail to stay
For coming in his pants at the local dance
With poor little Angeline

Now the window of his cell overlooked the dell
Where the squire was giving poor Angeline hell
As she lay on the grass, he recognized the arse
Of poor little Angeline

Now he got such a start that he let out a fart
Which blew the prison bars apart
And he ran like shit lest the squire should split
His poor little Angeline

When he got to the spot and saw what was what
He tied the villain's cock in a knot
As the squire lay on his guts he was kicked in the nuts
By poor little Angeline

'Oh, Blacksmith true, I love you, I do
And I can tell by your trousers that you love me too
Here I am undressed, come and do your best'
Cried poor little Angeline

No it won't take long to finish this song
For the blacksmith had a penis over one foot long
And his phallic charm was as brawny as his arm
Happy little Angeline

BIG FAT ARSE

Here's a song about something we've all seen
About a girl with everything
Looks and brains and personality
And more of something else than there ought to be

Living in a land of good and plenty here
We've got a lot of good food, wine and beer
Hard to keep trim with all that going on
But a single man must sing this song:

Hey look at those girls sitting over there
From here they look pretty fair
Look at them jugs, and those loose-fitting dresses
Tell-tale signs of a big, fat arse

A big, fat arse
A big fat arse
God damn I hate a big fat arse

So just stay put, we'll drink some beer
We can't be sure from over here
When she goes to the bog it will tell the tale
I told you so, it's a baby whale

A baby whale
A baby whale
I won't make a move on a baby whale

Here's another little verse about the same old thing
About this girl with everything
Looks and brains and personality
And more in back than what's meant for me

We're living in the land of good and plenty here
Too much food and wine and beer
Hard to keep fit with all that going on
But her boyfriend might just sing this song:

You know I don't mind the smoking or the halitosis
A few bad zits or a mild neurosis
A little B.O. or a flabby gut
But I just can't hack your big fat butt

Your big fat butt
Your big fat butt
Don't want to be seen with that big fat butt

Here's another little verse about the same old thing
About this girl with everything
Looks and brains and personality
And a rear like a five-ton GMC

We're living in the land of good and plenty here
Too much food and wine and beer
Hard to keep trim with all that going on
But a married man might just sing this song:

Now baby what the hell can I do?
To buy you dinner costs the price of two
To games, to shows, you need two seats
The city's planning wider seats

Wider walks
Wider seats
Now we've got to have wider streets

Well you broke my chair with those humongous hocks
The car's gotten four new overload shocks
You broke the toilet and an escalator
Now you've got to ride in the freight elevator

A freight elevator
And an escalator
You even crushed your new vibrator

Well about this girl with everything
This candidate for diary queen
She's pissed off now so I'll end this song
Get rid of them buns and we'll get it on

Get it on
Get it on
Get rid of them buns and we'll get it on

BYE, BYE BLACKBIRD

Once a boy was no good
Took a girl into the wood
Bye, bye blackbird

Laid her down upon the grass
Pinched her tits and slapped her arse
Bye, bye blackbird

Took her where nobody could find her
To a place where he could really grind her
Rolled her over on her front
Shoved his cock right up her cunt
Blackbird, bye, bye

But this girl was no sport
Took her story to a court
Bye, bye blackbird

Told her story in the morn
Judge and jury had the horn
Blackbird, bye, bye

Then the judge came to his decision
This poor fuck got eighteen years in prison
So next time, boy, do it right,
Stuff her crack full of dynamite
Blackbird, bye, bye